Edited by Jaume Llorens, Paloma Lozano García & Ryan Cockrell

SPANISH
SENTENCE BUILDERS
TRILOGY
PART 2
A lexicogrammar approach

SPEAKING BOOKLET

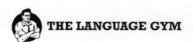
THE LANGUAGE GYM

About the authors

Gianfranco Conti taught for 25 years at schools in Italy, the UK and in Kuala Lumpur, Malaysia. He has also been a university lecturer, holds a Master's degree in Applied Linguistics and a PhD in metacognitive strategies as applied to second language writing. He is now an author, a popular independent educational consultant and professional development provider. He has written around 2,000 resources for the TES website, which have awarded him the Best Resources Contributor in 2015. He has co-authored the best-selling and influential book for world languages teachers, "The Language Teacher Toolkit" and "Breaking the sound barrier: Teaching learners how to listen", in which he puts forth his Listening As Modelling methodology. Gianfranco writes an influential blog on second language acquisition called The Language Gym, co-founded the interactive website language-gym.com and the Facebook professional group Global Innovative Language Teachers (GILT). Last but not least, Gianfranco has created the instructional approach known as E.P.I. (Extensive Processing Instruction).

Dylan Viñales has taught for 15 years, in schools in Bath, Beijing and Kuala Lumpur in state, independent and international settings. He lives in Kuala Lumpur. He is fluent in five languages, and gets by in several more. Dylan is, besides a teacher, a professional development provider, specialising in E.P.I., metacognition, teaching languages through music (especially ukulele) and cognitive science. In the last five years, together with Dr Conti, he has driven the implementation of E.P.I. in one of the top international schools in the world: Garden International School. This has allowed him to test, on a daily basis, the sequences and activities included in this book with excellent results (his students have won language competitions both locally and internationally). He has designed an original Spanish curriculum, bespoke instructional materials, based on Reading and Listening as Modelling (RAM and LAM). Dylan co-founded the fastest growing professional development group for modern languages teachers on Facebook, Global Innovative Languages Teachers, which includes over 12,000 teachers from all corners of the globe. He authors an influential blog on modern language pedagogy in which he supports the teaching of languages through E.P.I. Dylan is the lead author of Spanish content on the Language Gym website and oversees the technological development of the site.

Ben Levi is an innovative language specialist and has been working in the sector since 2018. With a background as a former professional tennis player, Ben's multicultural experiences, particularly in Spain during his formative years and extensive travel while competing globally, ignited his passion for languages. He achieved a 1st Class (Hons) degree in Language Studies and continues to research to develop his knowledge in the field of language learning. Fluent in Spanish and French (as well as English!), with proficiency in other languages, he employs a multifaceted approach to language education, integrating cultural immersion with the E.P.I. teaching methodology. Ben spearheaded the implementation of E.P.I. at his current school and supported curriculum planning in other secondary schools. He has also provided CPD on the effective implementation of E.P.I. to fellow professionals as well as how it can be adapted to other subjects. Active on social media platforms, Ben advocates for language enthusiasts and professionals through his channels, notably Ben Levi Languages on Facebook, Instagram and Twitter, where he shares valuable insights and resources. On TikTok, his engaging videos have engaged a wide audience, fostering language appreciation. Continuously innovating, Ben designs novel tasks and language games to inspire learners, nurturing their language proficiency and cultivating a passion for languages.

Acknowledgements

We would like to thank our editors, Paloma Lozano García, Jaume Llorens and Ryan Cockrell, for their tireless work, proofreading, editing and advising on this book. They are talented, accomplished professionals who work at the highest possible level and add value at every stage of the process. Not only this, but they are also lovely, good-humoured colleagues who go above and beyond, and make the hours of collaborating a real pleasure.

Thanks to Flaticon.com for providing access to a limitless library of engaging icons, clipart and images, which we have used to make this book more user-friendly and engaging for students.

As always, a huge shoutout to our team of incredible educators who helped in checking, and re-checking all the units of this volume: **Hannah Foote, Anneliese Yafai, Ester Borin, Catalina Petre, Barry Agnew, María Cristina Caroprese, Regina Vara Corella, Jérôme Nogues, Christian Moretti, Joe Barnes-Moran & Laura Gracia García.** It is thanks to your time, patience, professionalism and detailed feedback that we have been able to produce such a refined and highly accurate product. Your team spirit and good-humour throughout the process also make it a real pleasure to work together.

Finally, our gratitude to the MFL Twitterati for their ongoing support of E.P.I. and the Sentence Builders book series.

Gracias a todos,
Gianfranco, Dylan & Ben

Dedication

For Catrina
-Gianfranco

For Ariella & Leonard
-Dylan

For Olivia & Elsie
-Ben

Introduction

Hello and welcome to our second Speaking Skills book, designed to be an accompaniment to our Spanish, Extensive Processing Instruction course.

How to use this book

This book has been designed as a resource to use in conjunction with the E.P.I. approach and teaching strategies in a bid to scaffold oral communication by gradually moving from highly structured tasks (e.g. 'Oral Ping-Pong', 'No Snakes No Ladders', 'Communicative drills') to semi-structured ones (e.g. 'Surveys', 'Things in Common', 'Detectives and Informants').

The activities in this book should be carried out after an intensive listening and reading phase, in which the students have been flooded with highly comprehensible input containing the target vocabulary and grammar structures, thereby processing them receptively many times over.

If following the MARS EARS framework, teachers may want to stage two or three 'chunking-aloud' games, such as 'Mind reading', 'Sentence stealer', 'Lie detector', etc. in order to warm the students up, consolidate good pronunciation and refine their decoding skills.

Also, prior to playing oral retrieval practice games such as 'Oral Ping-Pong', it is recommended that the students do some retrieval practice in writing. This can be done through digital tools, worksheets, mini whiteboards and may be teacher and/or student led.

Finally, it is recommended that, before carrying out the fluency-building games 'Faster', 'Fast and Furious', 'Fluency cards' and Trapdoor', the students be given a few minutes to plan the tasks individually or with peers in order to decrease the potential for cognitive overload and subsequent errors that speaking at increasing speed rate may elicit due to the challenging nature of the task.

What's inside

The book contains 13 units which concern themselves with specific communicative functions, such as 'Saying what I do at home', 'Talking about my weekend plans' or 'Making after-school plans with a friend'.

Each unit includes a sentence builder with the target constructions and vocabulary followed by a series of tried and tested Conti E.P.I. speaking games, sequenced so as to pose a gradually increasing degree of challenge. The speaking games included are:

- Oral Ping-Pong
- Find Someone Who
- No Snakes No Ladders
- Staircase Translation
- Faster!
- Fast & Furious

- Communicative Drills
- Fluency Cards
- Trapdoor
- Things in Common
- Detectives & Informants
- Information Gap Tasks

As already noted, the above games are sequenced in ascending order of linguistic and cognitive challenge. The focus is on gradually building up students' fluency and autonomous competence. These games fall in the 'Structured Production', 'Routinization' and 'Spontaneity' phases in Dr Conti's **MARS EARS** pedagogical cycle, which is central to his E.P.I. approach.

Many thanks for reading this. We hope that both you and your students will find this book useful and enjoyable.

Gianfranco, Dylan & Ben

SENTENCE BUILDERS TRILOGY - PART 2

SPEAKING BOOKLET

TABLE OF CONTENTS

	TERM 1	
0	How to play the games - INSTRUCTIONS	**1**
1	Talking about the weather & free time	**3**
2	Talking about my daily routine & activities	**15**
3	Saying what I do at home	**27**
4	*OPTIONAL: Talking about the clothes & weather	**39**
5	My weekend plans – food & leisure	**51**
	TERM 2	
6	Saying where I live	**63**
7	Saying what I can do in my neighbourhood	**75**
8	Describing my street	**87**
9	Describing my home and furniture	**99**
	TERM 3	
10	Saying what I did in my neighbourhood	**111**
11	Saying what I did & am going to do at the weekend	**123**
12	Making after-school plans with a friend	**135**
13	*OPTIONAL: A future trip to Cádiz	**147**
* Units marked with an asterisk are optional		

THE LANGUAGE GYM

How to play the games – INSTRUCTIONS

ORAL PING-PONG

Students work with a partner.

1. Student A starts by reading out his/her first sentence **in English**. Student B must translate **into Spanish**.
2. Student A checks the answer on their sheet. If correct, Student B gets 3 points (100% accurate), 2 points (1 error), or 1 point (correct verb).
3. Student B then reads out his/her first sentence **in English**, Student A translates, and B checks and so on. It is called 'Oral ping-pong translation' because students are firing phrases at each other to translate and score points. **The person with the most points after 10 minutes wins.**

NOTE: As a follow-up, students should **write** the translations in the gaps provided.

FIND SOMEONE WHO

1. Students are each given a card and a grid to fill in (both provided in each unit of this book).
2. Students must take turns asking the key questions (also provided) and then listening to the information provided by fellow students on their cards.
3. If a student finds someone who matches the criteria in the grid, they write down the person's name.

NOTE: at times there will be **multiple people** who match a criterion, and at other times, there will be **red herrings** (cards which do not actually match any criteria at all). This is a design feature to create added challenge and engagement.

TIP: you will need to set high expectations and then monitor students to make sure they engage in target language and use their speaking & listening skills. Some students may try and bend the rules by copying from friends.

NO SNAKES NO LADDERS

Students work in triads. You will need one dice per table and a copy of both the English & Spanish board.

1. One student is the referee and two students are the players.
2. The referee has access to the translations (via a copy of either the English or the Spanish board).
3. Students role a dice and then move their counter forward. They must then translate the language in the box where their counter falls.
4. If a student translates correctly (as confirmed by the referee), they can roll again.
5. If a student cannot translate the content of a square, the referee must tell them the answer, and it is then the other player's turn.
6. When a student wins the game, the referee changes, in order to allow students to alternate roles.

TIP: We recommend starting from **Target Language to English**, and then, after a couple of rounds (or whenever students are ready), working from English to Target Language.

STAIRCASE TRANSLATION

Students work with a partner.

1. Students must **translate aloud** the paragraph as quickly as possible.
2. Once the whole paragraph has been successfully translated aloud, students write down the translation into the box.

FASTER

Students alternate the role of player and referee.

1. Students translate aloud a number of sentences in front of a referee.
2. The student referee provides a time score and some feedback on accuracy.
3. The student listens to feedback and then repeats the process with a second, third, fourth referee with an aim of improving in terms of speed and accuracy on each attempt.

 TIP: Make sure that referees have a visible timer to increase motivation!

 **THE LANGUAGE GYM**

FAST & FURIOUS
Similar to FASTER, but students work from gapped target language sentences.

COMMUNICATIVE DRILLS
Students alternate the role of player and referee.
1. Students work with a partner to translate short dialogues from English to Spanish.
2. The student referee monitors the game and provides help and feedback on accuracy.
3. Once the students have correctly translated all the boxes out loud, the game is over.
TIPS:
- We recommend a rule that whenever the game ends, the referee then faces the winner, or the loser.
- This game can be played with both players working together to translate the squares (collaborating and helping each other), or as a timed challenge (if students are more confident) to translate all 6/9 squares individually with the fastest time.

FLUENCY CARDS
Students alternate the role of player and referee.
Played like FASTER, students create sentences in the Target Language to match the content of the stimulus grid. There is a mixture of text and images in order to create varied & multi-modal connections to the lexical items and structures being studied.

THINGS IN COMMON
This activity works like the final SURVEY activity, but focuses on asking closed questions, such as "do you prefer *football* or *basketball?*"
1. Students are given some time to think about their own answers to the questions.
2. Students then ask their peers the questions and make a note of any students that have matching answers (hence 'things in common').
TIPS: Students can be given a set time to speak to as many of their peers as possible, or a race to find a certain number of people with a certain number of things in common.

TRAPDOOR
Students alternate the role of player and referee. Played like FASTER, students translate a set of sentences using the information in the table, which is chunked into several columns as a support.

DETECTIVES & INFORMANTS
This is a collaborative class game along the lines of **Find Someone Who**.
1. Divide the class into halves.
2. One half - **the detectives**: they have a grid with missing information that they need to fill in. There is one grid per team. This grid must stay at a central location, such as a team home base.
3. One half – **the informants**: they have the answers to the questions.
4. The detectives must ask questions to the informants and then return to their home base to help their team fill in the grid.

INFORMATION GAP TASK
Without viewing the other person's table, two students need to complete their own table by asking each other questions in Spanish in order to fill in the gaps.
1. Students take turns to ask each other questions and fill in the answers.
2. The game ends when both tables are fully filled in.

SURVEY
Students ask each other the key questions that have been practised throughout the unit. They then note down key information, either in English or in Spanish on their grid. As a follow-up you could ask students to write a summary of a friend's information, either in first or third person.

UNIT 1
Talking about weather and free time

¿Qué haces en tu tiempo libre?	*What do you do in your free time?*
¿Qué haces cuando hace buen/mal tiempo?	*What do you do when the weather is good/bad?*
¿Qué hace tu amigo en su tiempo libre?	*What does your friend do in his/her free time?*
¿Adónde vas los fines de semana?	*Where do you go at the weekend?*

A veces *Sometimes*

Entre semana
During the week

Los fines de semana
At the weekend

Cuando tengo tiempo
When I have time

Cuando está despejado
When the sky is clear

Cuando está nublado
When the sky is cloudy

Cuando hace buen tiempo
When the weather is good

Cuando hace mal tiempo
When the weather is bad

Cuando hace calor
When it's hot

Cuando hace frío
When it's cold

Cuando hace sol
When it's sunny

Cuando hace viento
When it's windy

Cuando hay niebla
When it's foggy

Cuando hay tormenta
When it's stormy

Cuando llueve
When it rains

Cuando nieva
When it snows

juego *I play*

mi amiga María juega
my friend María plays

al ajedrez	*chess*
a las cartas	*cards*
al baloncesto	*basketball*
al fútbol	*football*
al tenis	*tennis*
con mis amigos	*with my friends*
con sus amigos	*with his/her friends*

hago *I do*

mi amigo Lionel hace
my friend Lionel does

ciclismo	*cycling*
deporte	*sport*
equitación	*horse riding*
escalada	*rock climbing*
esquí	*skiing*
footing	*jogging*
los deberes	*homework*
natación	*swimming*
senderismo	*hiking*
vela	*sailing*

voy *I go*

mi amigo va
my friend (m) goes

mi amiga va
my friend (f) goes

a casa de mi amigo	*to my friend's house*
a casa de su amigo	*to his/her friend's house*
a la montaña	*to the mountain*
a la piscina	*to the pool*
a la playa	*to the beach*
al campo	*to the countryside*
al centro comercial	*to the shopping mall*
al gimnasio	*to the gym*
al parque	*to the park*
al polideportivo	*to the sports centre*
de marcha	*clubbing*
de paseo	*for a walk*
de pesca	*fishing*
en bici	*on a bike ride*

me quedo *I stay*

en mi casa	*in my home*
en mi dormitorio	*in my bedroom*

Felipe **María**	**se queda** *stays*	**en su casa**	*in his/her home*
		en su dormitorio	*in his/her bedroom*

THE LANGUAGE GYM

UNIT 1 – FIND SOMEONE WHO – Student Cards

A veces juego al ajedrez. **RAQUEL**	Entre semana mi amigo hace esquí. **JULIO**	Los fines de semana voy al parque. **MARINA**	Cuando hace buen tiempo juego al fútbol. **LUIGI**
Cuando está despejado mi amigo va de pesca. **VERÓNICA**	Cuando hace mal tiempo me quedo en casa. **BEN**	A veces juego al baloncesto con mi hermano. **OLIVIA**	Cuando tengo tiempo voy de compras en el centro comercial. **PALOMA**
Cuando hay niebla mi amiga va al polideportivo. **ROSITA**	Entre semana hago senderismo. **MARÍA**	Cuando hace calor hago natación. **PEDRO**	Cuando está nublado juego al tenis. **ELSIE**
Cuando nieva mi amigo hace esquí. **DINO**	Los fines de semana voy de marcha. **CARLOS**	Cuando hace mal tiempo me quedo en mi dormitorio. **PABLO**	A veces juego al baloncesto. **DAVID**

UNIT 1 – FIND SOMEONE WHO – Student Grid

¿Qué haces en tu tiempo libre?	*What do you do in your free time?*	
Find someone who...		**Name(s)**
1.	...plays football.	
2.	...goes clubbing at weekends.	
3.	...doesn't go out when the weather is bad.	
4.	...has a friend who goes fishing.	
5.	...sometimes plays basketball.	
6.	...goes shopping when they have time.	
7.	...sometimes plays chess.	
8.	...goes to the park at the weekend.	
9.	...plays tennis when its cloudy.	
10.	...goes swimming when it's hot.	
11.	...has a friend who does skiing.	
12.	...does hiking during the week.	
13.	...is a red herring. 🐟 (no match)	

THE LANGUAGE GYM

UNIT 1 – ORAL PING-PONG – Person A

ENGLISH	SPANISH
When the weather is bad, my friend (f) plays cards.	Cuando hace mal tiempo mi amiga juega a las cartas.
When it snows, I go skiing.	
When the weather is good, I go horse riding.	Cuando hace buen tiempo hago equitación.
When it's windy, I go to the shopping mall.	
When there is a storm, I stay at home.	Cuando hay tormenta me quedo en mi casa.
During the week, I play with my friends.	
When the sky is clear, I go to the gym.	Cuando está despejado voy al gimnasio.
When it's sunny, my friend (f) goes fishing.	
At the weekend, my friend (m) goes to the beach.	Los fines de semana mi amigo va a la playa.
When it's hot, Felipe stays in his room.	

UNIT 1 – ORAL PING-PONG – Person B

ENGLISH	SPANISH
When the weather is bad, my friend (f) plays cards.	
When it snows, I go skiing.	Cuando nieva hago esquí.
When the weather is good, I go horse riding.	
When it's windy, I go to the shopping mall.	Cuando hace viento voy al centro comercial.
When there is a storm, I stay at home.	
During the week, I play with my friends.	Entre semana juego con mis amigos.
When the sky is clear, I go to the gym.	
When it's sunny, my friend (f) goes fishing.	Cuando hace sol mi amiga va de pesca.
At the weekend, my friend (m) goes to the beach.	
When it's hot, Felipe stays in his room.	Cuando hace calor Felipe se queda en su dormitorio.

No Snakes No Ladders

 **START**	**1** When it's cold, my friend (m) goes skiing.	**2** When it's cloudy, I go swimming.	**3** When I have time, I play football.	**4** When it snows, my friend (m) plays with his friends.	**5** When it's foggy, my friend (f) plays cards.	**6** When it's sunny, I play tennis.	**7** When it's cloudy, my friend (m) plays cards.
15 When it's windy, my friend (m) rides a bike.	**14** When the weather is bad, my friend (f) goes to the gym.	**13** When the weather is good, I go to my friend's (m) house.	**12** When it's sunny, my friend (f) goes fishing.	**11** When the sky is clear, I go to the beach.	**10** At the weekend, my friend (f) does sport.	**9** When it rains, I play chess.	**8** When it's windy, my friend (f) does homework.
16 When it's hot, I go to the countryside.	**17** During the week, I stay at home.	**18** At the weekend, I go to the shopping mall.	**19** Sometimes, my friend (m) stays at home.	**20** When I have time, I play basketball.	**21** At the weekends, my friend (m) goes to the beach.	**22** When it snows, I go hiking.	**23** When it's stormy, my friend stays in his room.
FINISH	**30** When it rains, I go to the sports centre.	**29** When the sky is clear, I play tennis.	**28** During the week, I go to the gym.	**27** When I have time, I play football.	**26** On weekends, I go cycling.	**25** When the weather is bad, my friend (m) stays at home.	**24** Sometimes, my friend (m) goes rock climbing.

No Snakes No Ladders

SALIDA						
1 Cuando hace frío mi amigo hace esquí.	**2** Cuando está nublado hago natación.	**3** Cuando tengo tiempo juego al fútbol.	**4** Cuando nieva mi amigo juega con sus amigos.	**5** Cuando hay niebla mi amiga juega a las cartas.	**6** Cuando hace sol juego al tenis.	**7** Cuando está nublado mi amigo juega a las cartas.
15 Cuando hace viento mi amigo va en bici.	**14** Cuando hace mal tiempo mi amiga va al gimnasio.	**13** Cuando hace buen tiempo voy a casa de mi amigo.	**12** Cuando hace sol mi amiga va de pesca.	**11** Cuando está despejado voy a la playa.	**10** Los fines de semana mi amiga hace deporte.	**9** Cuando llueve juego al ajedrez.
16 Cuando hace calor voy al campo.	**17** Entre semana me quedo en casa.	**18** Los fines de semana voy al centro comercial.	**19** A veces mi amigo se queda en su casa.	**20** Cuando tengo tiempo juego al baloncesto.	**21** Los fines de semana mi amigo va a la playa.	**8** Cuando hace viento mi amiga hace los deberes.
LLEGADA	**30** Cuando llueve voy al polideportivo.	**29** Cuando está despejado juego al tenis.	**28** Entre semana voy al gimnasio.	**27** Cuando tengo tiempo juego al fútbol.	**26** Los fines de semana hago ciclismo.	**23** Cuando hay tormenta mi amigo se queda en su dormitorio.
					25 Cuando hace mal tiempo mi amigo se queda en su casa.	**24** A veces mi amigo hace escalada.

THE LANGUAGE GYM

8

UNIT 1 – STAIRCASE TRANSLATION

At the weekend

At the weekend, I play basketball.

At the weekend, I play basketball. During the week, my friend (m) goes to the shopping centre.

At the weekend, I play basketball. During the week, my friend goes to the shopping centre. When it rains I stay at home.

At the weekend, I play basketball. During the week, my friend goes to the shopping centre. When it rains, I stay at home. However (sin embargo), when it's sunny I do hiking.

At the weekend, I play basketball. During the week, my friend goes to the shopping centre. When it rains, I stay at home. However (sin embargo), when it's sunny I do hiking. What do you do in your free time?

Translate the final step here:

UNIT 1 – FASTER!

Say:

1. What do you do in your free time?

2. When I have time, I go to the gym.

3. During the week, I do my homework.

4. What do you do when the weather is bad?

5. When the weather is bad, I stay at home.

6. When it's sunny, I play tennis.

7. What do you do when it snows?

8. When it snows, I do skiing.

9. What does your friend do at the weekend?

10. At the weekend, my friend goes to the shopping mall.

	Time	Mistakes	Referee's name
1			
2			
3			
4			

UNIT 1 – FAST & FURIOUS – ROUND 1

1. Los _____ de semana _____ a casa de mi amigo.
   At the weekend, I go to my friend's house.

2. _____ hace buen _____ mi amigo va a la playa.
   When the weather is good, my friend goes to the beach.

3. Entre semana _____ los deberes en mi _____.
   During the week, I do homework in my room.

4. Cuando _____ tiempo _____ al polideportivo con _____ amigo.
   When I have time, I go to the sports centre with my friend.

5. Cuando _____ sol juego al tenis en el _____.
   When it's sunny, I play tennis in the park.

	Time 1	Time 2	Time 3	Time 4
Time				
Mistakes				

UNIT 1 – FAST & FURIOUS – ROUND 2

1. _____ hace frío mi amiga Olivia _____ a la montaña.
   When it's cold, my friend Olivia goes to the mountain.

2. Los fines de _____ hago _____ en la playa.
   At the weekend, I do jogging on the beach.

3. Cuando _____ me quedo en _____ y hago _____ deberes.
   When it rains, I stay in my home and I do my homework.

4. A veces mi _____ va _____ gimnasio y hace _____.
   Sometimes, my friend (m) goes to the gym and does sport.

5. _____ semana _____ está despejado voy en _____.
   During the week, when the sky is clear, I go on a bike ride.

	Time 1	Time 2	Time 3	Time 4
Time				
Mistakes				

THE LANGUAGE GYM

UNIT 1 – COMMUNICATIVE DRILLS

1	2	3
What do you do when it's cloudy? - When it's cloudy, I play chess with my friends. And you? **Sometimes, I stay at home when it's cloudy.** - Very good.	**What do you do in your free time?** - When I have time, I play tennis with my friends. **I also play tennis at the weekend.** - Good! I like tennis.	**What do you do when the weather is bad?** - I stay at home and do homework. **When the weather is bad, I go to my friend's house.**
4	**5**	**6**
What do you do when it's sunny? - When it's sunny, I go to the beach. And you? What do you do when it's sunny? **I really like the beach but when the weather is good, I go to the park.**	**What does your friend Elsie do when the weather is good?** - When the weather is good, my friend Elsie goes fishing. Do you go fishing? **No, when the weather is good, I play football.** - That's good!	**Where do you go at the weekend?** - At the weekend, I go to the mall with my family. **That's cool! And during the week?** - During the week, I do sport.
7	**8**	**9**
Where do you go during the week? - During the week I go to the gym with my friend Pedro. And you? What do you do during the week? **During the week, I play basketball at the sports centre.**	**Where does your friend Norberto go when the weather is bad?** - My friend Norberto stays at home when the weather is bad. And you? **Me too. When the weather is bad, I stay in my house.**	**What do you do at the weekend?** - At the weekend, I play basketball with my friends. **Very good! I love basketball.**

UNIT 1 – COMMUNICATIVE DRILLS
REFEREE CARD

1	2	3
¿Qué haces cuando está nublado? - Cuando está nublado juego al ajedrez con mis amigos. ¿Y tú? **A veces me quedo en casa cuando está nublado.** - Muy bien.	**¿Qué haces en tu tiempo libre?** - Cuando tengo tiempo juego al tenis con mis amigos. **También juego al tenis los fines de semana.** - ¡Bien! Me gusta el tenis.	**¿Qué haces cuando hace mal tiempo?** - Me quedo en casa y hago los deberes. **Cuando hace mal tiempo voy a casa de mi amigo.**

4	5	6
¿Qué haces cuando hace sol? - Cuando hace sol voy a la playa. ¿Y tú? ¿Qué haces cuando hace sol? **Me gusta mucho la playa, pero cuando hace buen tiempo voy al parque.**	**¿Qué hace tu amiga Elsie cuando hace buen tiempo?** - Cuando hace buen tiempo mi amiga Elsie va de pesca. ¿Vas de pesca? **No, cuando hace buen tiempo juego al fútbol.** - ¡Qué bien!	**¿Adónde vas los fines de semana?** - Los fines de semana voy al centro comercial con mi familia. **¡Qué guay! ¿Y entre semana?** - Entre semana hago deporte.

7	8	9
¿Adónde vas entre semana? - Entre semana voy al gimnasio con mi amigo Pedro. ¿Y tú? ¿Qué haces entre semana? **Entre semana juego al baloncesto en el polideportivo.**	**¿Adónde va tu amigo Norberto cuando hace mal tiempo?** - Mi amigo Norberto se queda en casa cuando hace mal tiempo. ¿Y tú? **Yo también. Cuando hace mal tiempo me quedo en mi casa.**	**¿Qué haces los fines de semana?** - Los fines de semana juego al baloncesto con mis amigos. **¡Muy bien! Me encanta el baloncesto.**

UNIT 1 – SURVEY

	¿Cómo te llamas? *What is your name?*	¿Qué haces en tu tiempo libre? *What do you do in your free time?*	¿Qué haces cuando hace sol? *What do you do when it's sunny?*	¿Qué haces en los fines de semana? *What do you do at the weekend?*
e.g.	*Me llamo Juan.*	*Cuando tengo tiempo voy al gimnasio.*	*Cuando hace sol voy a la playa.*	*Los fines de semana voy al centro comercial.*
1.				
2.				
3.				
4.				
5.				
6.				
7.				
8.				
9.				

THE LANGUAGE GYM

UNIT 1 – ANSWERS

FIND SOMEONE WHO

Find someone who...		Name(s)
1.	...plays football.	**Luigi**
2.	...goes clubbing at weekends.	**Carlos**
3.	...doesn't like to go out when the weather is bad.	**Ben/Pablo**
4.	...has a friend who goes fishing.	**Verónica**
5.	...sometimes plays basketball.	**Olivia/David**
6.	...goes shopping when they have time.	**Paloma**
7.	...sometimes plays chess.	**Raquel**
8.	...goes to the park at the weekend.	**Marina**
9.	...plays tennis when its cloudy.	**Elsie**
10.	...goes swimming when it's hot.	**Pedro**
11.	...has a friend who does skiing.	**Julio/Dino**
12.	...does hiking during the week.	**María**
13.	...is a red herring. 🐟 (no match)	**Rosita**

STAIRCASE TRANSLATION

Los fines de semana juego al baloncesto. Entre semana, mi amigo va al centro comercial. Cuando llueve me quedo en casa. Sin embargo, cuando hace sol hago senderismo. ¿Qué haces en tu tiempo libre?

FASTER!

REFEREE SOLUTION

1. ¿Qué haces en tu tiempo libre?   2. Cuando tengo tiempo voy al gimnasio.
3. Entre semana hago mis deberes.   4. ¿Qué haces cuando hace mal tiempo?
5. Cuando hace mal tiempo me quedo en casa.   6. Cuando hace sol juego al tenis.
7. ¿Qué haces cuando nieva?   8. Cuando nieva hago esquí.   9. ¿Qué hace tu amigo los fines de semana?
10. Los fines de semana mi amigo va al centro comercial.

FAST & FURIOUS

ROUND 1

1. Los **fines** de semana **voy** a casa de mi amigo.
2. **Cuando** hace buen **tiempo** mi amigo va a la playa.
3. Entre semana **hago** los deberes en mi **dormitorio**.
4. Cuando **tengo** tiempo voy al polideportivo con **mi** amigo.
5. Cuando **hace** sol juego al tenis en el **parque**.

ROUND 2

1. Cuando **hace** frío mi amiga Olivia **va** a la montaña.
2. Los fines de **semana** hago **footing** en la playa.
3. Cuando **llueve** me quedo en mi **casa** y hago **mis** deberes.
4. A veces mi **amigo** va **al** gimnasio y hace **deporte**.
5. **Entre** semana, **cuando** está despejado voy en **bici**.

UNIT 2. Talking about my daily routine & activities

¿A qué hora te levantas entre semana?	What time do you get up during the week?
¿Qué haces antes del colegio?	What do you do before school?
¿Qué haces cuando vuelves a casa?	What do you do when you return home?
¿Qué haces para ayudar en casa?	What do you do to help at home?

INSTRUCTIONS FOR ALL GAMES ARE ON **PAGES 1-2**

Entre semana *During the week*	me acuesto	*I go to bed*	**a la una**			
	me ducho	*I shower*	**a las**	dos		
	me lavo los dientes	*I brush my teeth*		tres		
	me levanto	*I get up*		cuatro	**y cuarto** *quarter past*	
	me meto en internet	*I go on the internet*		cinco		
	me peino	*I brush my hair*		seis		
	me pongo el uniforme	*I put on my uniform*		siete	**y media** *half past*	
Antes del colegio *Before school*	me visto	*I get dressed*		ocho		
Por la mañana *In the morning*	almuerzo	*I have lunch*		nueve	**menos cuarto** *quarter to*	
	ceno	*I have dinner*		diez		
	descanso	*I rest*		once		
	desayuno cereales	*I have cereal for breakfast*				
	hago mis deberes	*I do my homework*				
	hago pesas	*I lift weights*				
Por la tarde *In the afternoon/ evening*	juego a videojuegos	*I play videogames*				
	leo un libro	*I read a book*				
	mirar escaparates	*go window shopping*				
	preparo mi mochila	*I get my bag ready*				
Por la noche *At night*	salgo de casa	*I leave the house*	**a**	**mediodía** *midday*		
	tomo el desayuno	*I have breakfast*				
	voy al colegio	*I go to school*				
	veo la tele	*I watch television*		**medianoche** *midnight*		
	vuelvo a casa	*I return home*				

pero *but*	**hoy** *today*	**(no) debo** *I must (not)*	**ayudar en casa**	*help at home*
		puedo *I can*	**hacer la cama**	*make the bed*
			hacer las tareas domésticas	*do the chores*
sin embargo *however*	**esta tarde** *this afternoon / evening*	**quiero** *I want to*	**hacer mis deberes**	*do my homework*
		tengo que *I have to*	**ir al colegio**	*go to school*
		voy a *I'm going to*	**levantarme temprano**	*get up early*
y *and*			**salir** *go out* / **con** *with* / **mi amigo** *my friend (m)* **mi amiga** *my friend (f)*	

Author's notes:
1) The verbs ***debo/puedo/quiero*** fall into a special category known as "modal verbs". These are used to say what you "must", "can" or "want to" do. ***Voy a*** is used for the near future.
2) The activities have been arranged by reflexives and non-reflexives. They are organised alphabetically for ease of use. This means that "me acuesto" is first on the list... although usually the last activity in the day :)

THE LANGUAGE GYM

UNIT 2 – FIND SOMEONE WHO – Student Cards

Entre semana me levanto a las seis. **PEDRO**	Por la tarde hago mis deberes a las cuatro y media. **JUAN**	Entre semana desayuno cereales a las siete. **JULIA**	Esta tarde voy a ayudar en casa y hacer la cama. **MIGUEL**
Por la mañana me ducho a las siete y cuarto. **ALEJANDRA**	Por la mañana salgo de casa a las ocho. **MARCOS**	Almuerzo a mediodía. **FELIPE**	Siempre me ducho a las siete y cuarto. **OLIVIA**
Antes del colegio me pongo el uniforme a las siete menos cuarto. **PABLO**	Por la mañana me visto a las once y cuarto. **RAFAEL**	Entre semana me levanto a las seis. **EDSON**	Esta tarde puedo salir con mis amigas. **ADA**
Entre semana voy al colegio a las ocho menos cuarto. **SIMÓN**	Creo que debo ayudar en casa. **MARÍA**	Pues, esta tarde voy a salir con mi amigo. **CARMEN**	Hoy debo ayudar en casa. **LUIS**

UNIT 2 – FIND SOMEONE WHO – Student Grid

¿Qué haces antes/después del colegio?		*What do you do before/after school?*	
Find someone who...			**Name(s)**
1.	...does their homework in the afternoon.		
2.	...leaves home at 8:00 in the morning.		
3.	...can go out with their friends this afternoon.		
4.	...must help at home.		
5.	...gets up at 6:00 during the week.		
6.	...is going to make their bed.		
7.	...has lunch at midday.		
8.	...showers at 7:15 in the morning.		
9.	...goes to school at 7:45 in the morning.		
10.	...eats breakfast at 7:00 in the morning.		
11.	...is going to go out with a friend this afternoon.		
12.	...gets dressed late in the morning.		
13.	...is a red herring. 🐟 (no match)		

UNIT 2 – ORAL PING-PONG – Person A

ENGLISH	SPANISH
In the morning, I get up at 6:00.	
In the afternoon, I do my homework at 4:00.	Por la tarde hago mis deberes a las cuatro.
Before school, I put on my uniform at 7:00.	.
However, this afternoon, I have to help at home.	Sin embargo, esta tarde tengo que ayudar en casa.
At night, I watch television at 10:00.	
What do you do before school?	¿Qué haces antes del colegio?
During the week, I go on the internet at 3:00 p.m.	
In the afternoon, I read a book, but today, I want to go out with my friend.	Por la tarde leo un libro, pero hoy quiero salir con mi amigo.
What time do you get up during the week?	
In the morning, I have cereal for breakfast.	Por la mañana desayuno cereales.

UNIT 2 – ORAL PING-PONG – Person B

ENGLISH	SPANISH
In the morning, I get up at 6:00.	Por la mañana me levanto a las seis.
In the afternoon, I do my homework at 4:00.	
Before school, I put on my uniform at 7:00.	Antes del colegio me pongo el uniforme a las siete.
However, this afternoon I have to help at home.	
At night, I watch television at 10:00.	Por la noche veo la tele a las diez.
What do you do before school?	
During the week, I go on the internet at 3:00 p.m.	Entre semana me meto en internet a las tres de la tarde.
In the afternoon, I read a book, but today, I want to go out with my friend.	
What time do you get up during the week?	¿A qué hora te levantas entre semana?
In the morning, I have cereal for breakfast.	

No Snakes No Ladders

7 In the afternoon, I play videogames at 4:00.	**6** During the week, I do my homework at 3:30.	**5** In the morning, I have breakfast at 8:00.	**4** In the morning, I go to school at 9:00.	**3** During the week, I have lunch at midday.	**2** At night, I watch TV at 10:00.	**1** In the afternoon, I go out with my friends at 5:00.
8 At night, I go to bed at 11:00.	**9** Before school, I get dressed at 7:00.	**10** In the afternoon, I leave the house at 3:00...	**11** ...but today, I have to do my homework.	**12** At night, I go on the internet at 8:30.	**13** In the morning, I read a book at 11:00...	**14** ...but today, I am going out with my friend.
23 During the week, I have lunch at 12:00.	**22** In the afternoon, I pack my bag at 4:00.	**21** At night, I have dinner at 7:00.	**20** At night, I go to bed at midnight, but today, I must not.	**19** However, today, I am going to help at home.	**18** In the afternoon, I rest at 2:00.	**17** In the morning, I get dressed at 6:15.
24 Before school, I brush my hair and put on my uniform.	**25** At night, I play videogames at 10:30.	**26** However, today, I have to get up early.	**27** In the afternoon, I return home at 6:00.	**28** In the morning, I have cereal for breakfast at 7:00.	**29** At night, I go to bed at midnight.	**30** At night, I study at 9:00, but today, I am going to go out.

START

15 At night, I brush my teeth at 10:00.

16 In the afternoon, I rest at 4:00.

FINISH

UNIT 2

No Snakes No Ladders

15 Por la noche me lavo los dientes a las diez.	**SALIDA**	**1** Por la tarde salgo con mis amigos a las cinco.	**2** Por la noche veo la tele a las diez.	**3** Entre semana almuerzo a mediodía.	**4** Por la mañana voy al colegio a las nueve.	**5** Por la mañana tomo el desayuno a las ocho.	**6** Entre semana hago mis deberes a las tres y media.	**7** Por la tarde juego a videojuegos a las cuatro.
16 Por la tarde descanso a las cuatro.	**14** ...pero hoy voy a salir con mi amigo.	**13** Por la mañana leo un libro a las once...	**12** Por la noche me meto en internet a las ocho y media.	**11** ...pero hoy tengo que hacer mis deberes.	**10** Por la tarde salgo de casa a las tres...	**9** Antes del colegio me visto a las siete.	**8** Por la noche me acuesto a las once.
17 Por la mañana me visto a las seis y cuarto.	**18** Por la tarde descanso a las dos.	**19** Sin embargo, hoy voy a ayudar en casa.	**20** Por la noche me acuesto a medianoche, pero hoy no debo.	**21** Por la noche ceno a las siete.	**22** Por la tarde preparo mi mochila a las cuatro.	**23** Entre semana almuerzo a las doce.
30 Por la noche estudio a las nueve pero hoy voy a salir.	**29** Por la noche me acuesto a medianoche.	**28** Por la mañana desayuno cereales a las siete.	**27** Por la tarde vuelvo a casa a las seis.	**26** Sin embargo, hoy tengo que levantarme temprano.	**25** Por la noche juego a videojuegos a las diez y media.	**24** Antes del colegio me peino y me pongo el uniforme.
LLEGADA

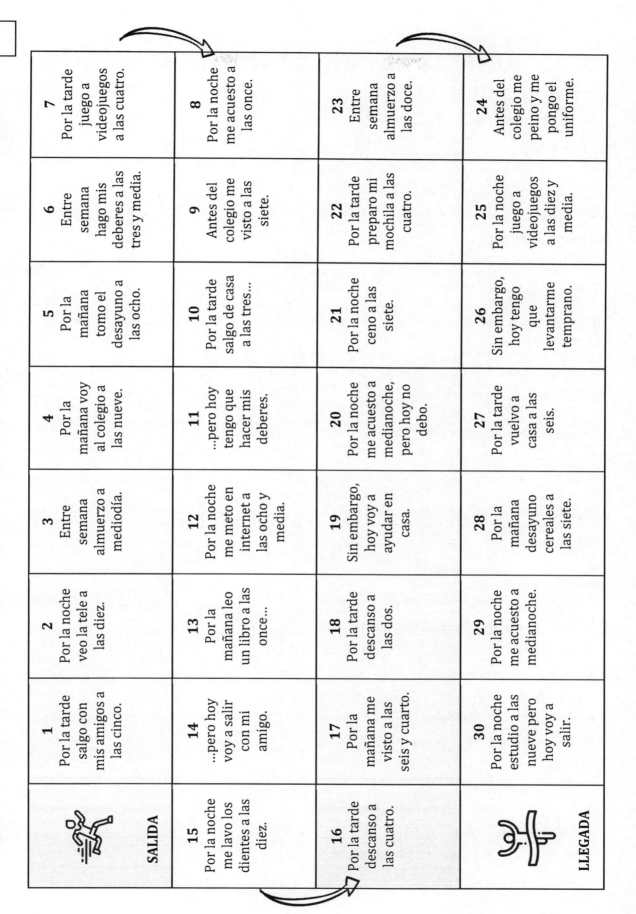

 THE LANGUAGE GYM

20

UNIT 2 – STAIRCASE TRANSLATION

In the afternoon

In the afternoon, I go on the internet.

In the afternoon, I go on the internet at 5:30.

In the afternoon, I go on the internet at 5:30, but today, I have to help at home.

In the afternoon, I go on the internet at 5:30, but today, I have to help at home. In the morning, I get dressed at 6:45.

In the afternoon, I go on the internet at 5:30, but today, I have to help at home. In the morning, I get dressed at 6:45. What time do you get up during the week?

Translate the last step here:

UNIT 2 – FASTER!

Say:

1. What time do you get up during the week?

2. Before school, I brush my teeth at 7:15.

3. In the morning, I have cereal for breakfast.

4. What do you do before school?

5. In the afternoon, I read a book, but today, I have to go out with a friend.

6. In the morning, I leave the house at 8:30.

7. During the week, I get up at 9:00, but today, I have to get up early.

8. What do you do when you return home?

9. At night, I have dinner at 8:30.

10. Before school, I shower, and I put on my uniform.

	Time	Mistakes	Referee's name
1			
2			
3			
4			

UNIT 2 – TRAPDOOR

Entre semana	me acuesto	a la	una					ayudar en casa
	me ducho				pero			hacer las tareas domésticas
Antes del colegio	me lavo los dientes		dos tres cuatro cinco seis siete ocho nueve diez once	y cuarto	sin embargo	hoy	(no) debo	hacer mis deberes
Por la mañana	me levanto			y media		esta tarde	puedo	hacer la cama
	me meto en internet	a las		menos	y		quiero	ir al colegio
Por la tarde	me peino			cuarto			tengo que	levantarme temprano
Por la noche	me pongo el uniforme						voy a	salir con mi amigo
	me visto							

ROUND 1

1. During the week, I get up at 7:30, but today, I have to get up early.
2. In the morning, I shower at 10:15, and today, I want to help at home.
3. At night, I go on the internet at 10:30, but this afternoon, I must go out with my friend.
4. In the morning, I get dressed at 5:45, and today, I'm going to make the bed.
5. Before school, I brush my hair at 7:45. However, today, I want to do the chores.
6. At night, I go to bed at 11:15. However, this afternoon, I can go out with my friend.
7. During the week, I watch TV at 8:00, but today, I'm going to do my homework.

	Time 1	Time 2	Time 3	Time 4
Time				
Mistakes				

ROUND 2

1. In the morning, I have cereal for breakfast at 7:15, but today, I must make my bed.
2. In the afternoon, I play videogames at 5:00. However, this afternoon, I have to do the chores.
3. At night, I have dinner at 8:30, and today, I am going to go out with a friend.
4. Before school, I have breakfast at 6:30, and today, I want to make the bed.
5. During the week, I watch television at 7:00, but this afternoon, I'm going to do my homework.
6. Before school, I read a book at 6:30, but today, I have to go to school early.
7. In the afternoon, I return home at 3:45, and today, I want to go out with my friend.

	Time 1	Time 2	Time 3	Time 4
Time				
Mistakes				

UNIT 2 – COMMUNICATIVE DRILLS

1	2	3
What do you do before school? - Before school, I get up and shower. And you? **In the morning, I get dressed at 7:30 and go to school.** - I also get dressed at 7:30.	**What do you do to help at home?** - In the afternoon, I have to do household chores, and today, I am going to make the bed. **What do you do during the week?** - During the week, I watch TV and play videogames.	**What do you do when you come back home?** - In the afternoon, I rest at 4:30, but this evening, I am going to do my homework. And you? **In the evening, I read a book and rest. However, today, I must help at home.**
4	**5**	**6**
At what time do you get up during the week? - During the week, I get up at 7:00. However, today, I want to get up early. **What do you do before school?** - Before school, I have cereal for breakfast at 7:45 and put on my uniform.	**What do you do during the week?** - During the week, I get my bag ready and go on the internet. However, this afternoon, I have to do household chores. And you? **Before school, I brush my hair and get dressed at 6:15, but today, I have to make the bed.**	**What do you do at night?** - At night, I play videogames at 11:30. However, tonight, I can go out with a friend. **At what time do you get up during the week?** - During the week, I get up at 5:30. And you? **In the morning, I get up at five!**
7	**8**	**9**
What do you do when you come back home? - When I come back home, I go on the internet and play videogames. **What do you do to help at home?** - I have to do household chores.	**What do you do during the week?** - During the week, I leave the house at 6:15. However, today, I don't have to go to school. And you? **During the week, I watch TV at quarter to nine, but tonight, I am going to help at home.** - This afternoon, I am going to help at home and do household chores.	**What do you do in the evening?** - In the evening, I come back home at 5:00 and have dinner at 7:00. **What do you do at night?** - At night, I go to bed at 9:00, but tonight, I am going out with a friend. What do you do at night? - At night, I go on the internet and I have a shower.

1	2	3
¿Qué haces antes del colegio? - Antes del colegio me levanto y me ducho. ¿Y tú? **Por la mañana me visto a las siete y media y voy al colegio.** - Yo también me visto a las siete y media.	**¿Qué haces para ayudar en casa?** - Por la tarde tengo que hacer las tareas domésticas y hoy voy a hacer la cama. **¿Qué haces entre semana?** - Entre semana veo la tele y juego a videojuegos.	**¿Qué haces cuando vuelves a casa?** - Por la tarde descanso a las cuatro y media pero esta tarde voy a hacer mis deberes. ¿Y tú? **Por la noche leo un libro y descanso, sin embargo, hoy debo ayudar en casa.**
4	**5**	**6**
¿A qué hora te levantas entre semana? - Entre semana me levanto a las siete, sin embargo hoy quiero levantarme temprano. **¿Qué haces antes del colegio?** - Antes del colegio desayuno cereales a las ocho menos cuarto y me pongo el uniforme.	**¿Qué haces entre semana?** - Entre semana preparo mi mochila y me meto en internet, sin embargo esta tarde tengo que hacer las tareas domésticas. ¿Y tú? **Antes del colegio me peino y me visto a las seis y cuarto pero hoy debo hacer la cama.**	**¿Qué haces por la noche?** - Por la noche juego a videojuegos a las once y media sin embargo esta noche puedo salir con un amigo. **¿A qué hora te levantas entre semana?** - Entre semana me levanto a las cinco y media. ¿Y tú? **¡Por la mañana me levanto a las cinco!**
7	**8**	**9**
¿Qué haces cuando vuelves a casa? - Cuando vuelvo a casa me meto en internet y juego a videojuegos. **¿Qué haces para ayudar en casa?** - Tengo que hacer las tareas domésticas.	**¿Qué haces entre semana?** - Entre semana salgo de casa a las seis y cuarto, sin embargo hoy no tengo que ir al colegio. ¿Y tú? **Entre semana veo la tele a las nueve menos cuarto, pero esta noche voy a ayudar en casa.** Esta tarde voy a ayudar en casa y hacer las tareas domésticas.	**¿Qué haces por la tarde?** - Por la tarde vuelvo a casa a las cinco y ceno a las siete. **¿Qué haces por la noche?** - Por la noche me acuesto a las nueve pero esta noche voy a salir con un amigo. ¿Qué haces por la noche? **Por la noche me meto en internet y me ducho.**

UNIT 2 – SURVEY

	¿Cómo te llamas? *What is your name?*	¿A qué hora te levantas entre semana? *What time do you get up during the week?*	¿Qué haces antes del colegio? *What do you do before school?*	¿Qué haces por la tarde? *What do you do in the afternoon?*	¿Qué haces entre semana? *What do you do during the week?*
e.g.	*Me llamo Juan.*	*Entre semana me levanto a las seis menos cuarto.*	*Antes del colegio me pongo el uniforme a las siete.*	*Por la tarde juego a videojuegos a las cinco.*	*Entre semana hago mis deberes a las cuatro y media.*
1.					
2.					
3.					
4.					
5.					
6.					
7.					

UNIT 2 – ANSWERS

FIND SOMEONE WHO

Find someone who...	Name(s)
1. ...does their homework in the afternoon.	**Juan**
2. ...leaves home at 8:00 in the morning.	**Marcos**
3. ...can go out with their friends this afternoon.	**Ada**
4. ...must help at home.	**María/Luis**
5. ...gets up at 6:00 during the week.	**Pedro/Edson**
6. ...is going to make their bed.	**Miguel**
7. ...has lunch at midday.	**Felipe**
8. ...showers at 7:15 in the morning.	**Alejandra/Olivia**
9. ...goes to school at 7:45 in the morning.	**Simón**
10. ...eats breakfast at 7:00 in the morning.	**Julia**
11. ...is going to go out with a friend this afternoon.	**Carmen**
12. ...gets dressed late in the morning.	**Rafael**
13. ...is a red herring. 🐟 (no match)	**Pablo**

STAIRCASE TRANSLATION

Por la tarde, me meto en internet a las cinco y media, pero hoy tengo que ayudar en casa. Por la mañana, me visto a las siete menos cuarto. ¿A qué hora te levantas entre semana?

FASTER!

REFEREE SOLUTION:

1. ¿A qué hora te levantas entre semana?   2. Antes del colegio me lavo los dientes a las siete y cuarto.
3. Por la mañana desayuno cereales.   4. ¿Qué haces antes del colegio?
5. Por la tarde leo un libro, pero hoy tengo que salir con un amigo.
6. Por la mañana salgo de casa a las ocho y media.
7. Entre semana me levanto a las nueve, pero hoy tengo que levantarme temprano.
8. ¿Qué haces cuando vuelves a casa?
9. Por la noche ceno a las ocho y media.   10. Antes del colegio me ducho y me pongo el uniforme

TRAPDOOR

ROUND 1

1. Entre semana me levanto a las siete y media pero hoy tengo que levantarme temprano.
2. Por la mañana me ducho a las diez y cuarto y hoy quiero ayudar en casa.
3. Por la noche me meto en internet a las diez y media pero esta tarde debo salir con mi amigo.
4. Por la mañana me visto a las seis menos cuarto y hoy voy a hacer la cama.
5. Antes del colegio me peino a las ocho menos cuarto, sin embargo, hoy quiero hacer las tareas domésticas.
6. Por la noche me acuesto a las once y cuarto. Sin embargo, esta tarde puedo salir con mi amigo.
7. Entre semana veo la tele a las ocho, pero hoy voy a hacer mis deberes.

ROUND 2

1. Por la mañana desayuno cereales a las siete y cuarto, pero hoy debo hacer la cama.
2. Por la tarde juego a videojuegos a las cinco sin embargo esta tarde debo hacer las tareas domésticas.
3. Por la noche ceno a las ocho y media y hoy voy a salir con un amigo.
4. Antes del colegio tomo el desayuno a las seis y media y hoy quiero hacer la cama.
5. Entre semana veo la tele a las siete, pero esta tarde voy a hacer mis deberes.
6. Antes del colegio leo un libro a las seis y media, pero hoy tengo que ir al colegio temprano.
7. Por la tarde vuelvo a casa a las cuatro menos cuarto y hoy quiero salir con mi amigo.

UNIT 3. Saying what I do at home

¿Qué haces en tu tiempo libre?	What do you do in your free time?
¿Qué haces en tu dormitorio?	What do you do in your bedroom?
¿Con qué frecuencia (lo haces)?	How frequently (do you do it)?

A eso de las seis de la mañana *At around 6 a.m.* **A menudo** *Often* **A veces** *Sometimes* **Cuando tengo tiempo** *When I have time* **Dos veces a la semana** *Twice a week* **Nunca** *Never* **Por lo general** *Usually* **Siempre** *Always* **Todos los días** *Every day*	**charlo con mi madre** ***chateo por WhatsApp** **desayuno** **descanso** **escucho música** **hago mis deberes** **juego a la Play** **leo revistas** **leo tebeos** **me ducho** **me lavo los dientes** **me meto en internet** **me visto** **monto en bici** **preparo la comida** **salgo de casa** **subo fotos a Instagram** **veo la tele** **veo películas** **veo series en Netflix**	*I chat with my mum* *I chat on WhatsApp* *I have breakfast* *I rest* *I listen to music* *I do my homework* *I play on the PlayStation* *I read magazines* *I read comics* *I shower* *I brush my teeth* *I go on the internet* *I get dressed* *I ride my bike* *I prepare food* *I leave the house* *I upload pics to Instagram* *I watch television* *I watch films/movies* *I watch series on Netflix*	**en la cocina** *in the kitchen* **en el comedor** *in the dining room* **en el cuarto de baño** *in the bathroom* **en el dormitorio de mi hermano** *in my brother's room* **en el dormitorio de mis padres** *in my parents' bedroom* **en mi dormitorio** *in my bedroom* **en el garaje** *in the garage* **en el jardín** *in the garden* **en la sala de juegos** *in the games room* **en el salón** *in the living room* **en la terraza** *on the terrace*

Author's note: there are two verbs in Spanish, **"charlar"** and **"chatear"**, which both mean *to chat*. We use **"charlar"** to refer to a spoken conversation and as a synonym of **"hablar"** *to talk*. **"Chatear"** usually refers to an online, text-based messaging, kind of chat.

UNIT 3 – FIND SOMEONE WHO – Student Cards

A eso de las seis de la mañana desayuno en la cocina. **PEDRO**	Por lo general, veo series en Netflix en la sala de juegos. **JUAN**	Todos los días descanso en el comedor. **JULIA**	A menudo preparo la comida en la cocina. **PEPE**
Dos veces a la semana juego a la Play en el salón. **NANCY**	A menudo leo revistas en la terraza. **MARÍA**	A veces monto en bici en el jardín. **PABLO**	Cuando tengo tiempo subo fotos a Instagram en la terraza. **ALEJANDRO**
Cuando tengo tiempo charlo con mi madre en el jardín. **JAMES**	Cuando tengo tiempo me meto en internet en mi dormitorio. **DANIEL**	Por lo general, veo películas en la sala de juegos. **AMELIA**	Nunca veo la tele en el garaje. **CATALINA**
Siempre leo revistas en la terraza. **FELIPE**	Por la mañana desayuno en la cocina. **MARTA**	Siempre monto en bici en el jardín con mis hermanos. **JORGE**	Todos los días veo la tele en el salón. **DAVID**

UNIT 3 – FIND SOMEONE WHO – Student Grid

¿Qué haces en tu tiempo libre?		*What do you do in your free time?*
Find someone who...		**Name(s)**
1.	...rests every day in the dining room.	
2.	...plays on the PlayStation in the living room.	
3.	...watches television in the living room.	
4.	...reads magazines on the terrace.	
5.	...uploads pics to Instagram.	
6.	...usually watches films in the games room.	
7.	...rides their bike.	
8.	...often prepares food in the kitchen.	
9.	...has breakfast in the kitchen at around 6:00 a.m.	
10.	...always goes on the internet in their bedroom.	
11.	...always chats with their mother in the garden.	
12.	...usually watches series on Netflix in the games room.	
13.	...never watches television in the garage.	

ENGLISH	SPANISH	ENGLISH	SPANISH
What do you do in your free time?	¿Qué haces en tu tiempo libre?	At around 6:00 a.m., I get dressed in my bedroom.	A eso de las seis de la mañana me visto en mi dormitorio.
At around 6:00 a.m., I have breakfast in the kitchen.		Twice a week, I prepare food in the kitchen.	
I always chat with my mum in my parents' bedroom.	Siempre charlo con mi madre en el dormitorio de mis padres.	Sometimes, I watch series on Netflix in the living room.	A veces veo series en Netflix en el salón.
Every day, I watch television in the dining room.		I always do my homework in the games room.	
Sometimes, I ride my bike in the garden.	A veces monto en bici en el jardín.	When I have time, I read comics in the garage.	Cuando tengo tiempo leo tebeos en el garaje.
I never watch films in the living room.		What do you do in your bedroom?	
Twice a week, I play on the PlayStation in the games room.	Dos veces a la semana juego a la Play en la sala de juegos.	Often, I read magazines on the terrace.	A menudo leo revistas en la terraza.
Often, I listen to music on the terrace.		I never go on the internet in the garage.	
When I have time, I upload pics to Instagram in the kitchen.	Cuando tengo tiempo subo fotos a Instagram en la cocina.	Usually, I chat on WhatsApp in the dining room.	Por lo general, chateo por WhatsApp en el comedor.
Usually, I rest in my brother's bedroom.		I always eat breakfast on the terrace.	

UNIT 3 – ORAL PING-PONG – Person B

ENGLISH	SPANISH	ENGLISH	SPANISH
What do you do in your free time?		At around 6:00 a.m., I get dressed in my bedroom.	
At around 6:00 a.m., I have breakfast in the kitchen.	A eso de las seis de la mañana desayuno en la cocina.	Twice a week, I prepare food in the kitchen.	Dos veces a la semana preparo la comida en la cocina.
I always chat with my mum in my parents' bedroom.		Sometimes, I watch series on Netflix in the living room.	
Every day, I watch television in the dining room.	Todos los días veo la tele en el comedor.	I always do my homework in the games room.	Siempre hago mis deberes en la sala de juegos.
Sometimes, I ride my bike in the garden.		When I have time, I read comics in the garage.	
I never watch films in the living room.	Nunca veo películas en el salón.	What do you do in your bedroom?	¿Qué haces en tu dormitorio?
Twice a week, I play on the PlayStation in the games room.		Often, I read magazines on the terrace.	
Often, I listen to music on the terrace.	A menudo escucho música en la terraza.	I never go on the internet in the garage.	Nunca me meto en internet en el garaje.
When I have time, I upload pics to Instagram in the kitchen.		Usually, I chat on WhatsApp in the dining room.	
Usually, I rest in my brother's bedroom.	Por lo general, descanso en el dormitorio de mi hermano.	I always eat breakfast on the terrace.	Siempre desayuno en la terraza.

 THE LANGUAGE GYM

UNIT 3

No Snakes No Ladders

START						
1 I always go on the internet in the living room.	**2** Often, I read comics in my bedroom.	**3** Usually, I watch TV in the dining room.	**4** When I have time, I upload pics to Instagram on the terrace.	**5** Sometimes, I rest in the garden.	**6** Every day, I play on the PlayStation in the games room.	**7** At around 6:00 a.m, I brush my teeth in the bathroom.
14 Sometimes, I ride my bike in the garden.	**13** I always watch series on Netflix in my bedroom.	**12** Usually, I have breakfast in the kitchen.	**11** I never chat on WhatsApp in the living room.	**10** When I have time, I watch movies in the living room.	**9** I never play on the PlayStation in the garage.	**8** What do you do in your free time?
17 How often do you do it?	**18** Sometimes, I rest in the games room.	**19** Usually, I watch TV in the living room.	**20** I always brush my teeth in the bathroom.	**21** Every day, I listen to music in the garden.	**22** Often, I get dressed in my bedroom.	**23** When I have time, I prepare food in the kitchen.
16 Every day, I shower in the bathroom.	**29** Sometimes, I watch series on Netflix in the living room.	**28** Twice a week, I chat with my mum in the garden.	**27** Every day, I read magazines in the games room.	**26** Often, I watch TV in my parents' bedroom.	**25** I always go on the internet in my bedroom.	**24** At around 6:00 a.m, I have cereal for breakfast in the kitchen.
15 Twice a week, I upload photos to Instagram in the dining room.	**30** When I have time, I brush my teeth in the bathroom.	FINISH				

THE LANGUAGE GYM

No Snakes No Ladders

SALIDA

1
Siempre me meto en internet en el salón.

2
A menudo leo tebeos en mi dormitorio.

3
Por lo general, veo la tele en el comedor.

4
Cuando tengo tiempo subo fotos a Instagram en la terraza.

5
A veces descanso en el jardín.

6
Todos los días juego a la Play en la sala de juegos.

7
A eso de las seis de la mañana me lavo los dientes en el cuarto de baño.

8
¿Qué haces en tu tiempo libre?

9
Nunca juego a la Play en el garaje.

10
Cuando tengo tiempo veo películas en el salón.

11
Nunca chateo por WhatsApp en el salón.

12
Por lo general, desayuno en la cocina.

13
Siempre veo series en Netflix en mi dormitorio.

14
A veces monto en bici en el jardín.

15
Dos veces a la semana subo fotos a Instagram en el comedor.

16
Todos los días me ducho en el cuarto de baño.

17
¿Con qué frecuencia (lo haces)?

18
A veces descanso en la sala de juegos.

19
Por lo general, veo la tele en el salón.

20
Siempre me lavo los dientes en el cuarto de baño.

21
Todos los días escucho música en el jardín.

22
A menudo me visto en mi dormitorio.

23
Cuando tengo tiempo preparo la comida en la cocina.

24
A eso de las seis de la mañana desayuno cereales en la cocina.

25
Siempre me meto en internet en mi dormitorio.

26
A menudo veo la tele en el dormitorio de mis padres.

27
Todos los días leo revistas en la sala de juegos.

28
Dos veces a la semana charlo con mi madre en el jardín.

29
A veces veo series en Netflix en el salón.

30
Cuando tengo tiempo me lavo los dientes en el cuarto de baño.

LLEGADA

THE LANGUAGE GYM

UNIT 3 – STAIRCASE TRANSLATION

Every day

Every day, I watch television in the living room.

Every day, I watch television in the living room. When I have time, I listen to music.

Every day, I watch television in the living room. When I have time, I listen to music in my bedroom. Twice a week, I upload pics to Instagram.

Every day, I watch television in the living room. When I have time, I listen to music in my bedroom. Twice a week, I upload pics to Instagram in the garden. I never ride my bike.

Every day, I watch television in the living room. When I have time, I listen to music in my bedroom. Twice a week, I upload pics to Instagram in the garden. I never ride my bike. What do you do in your free time?

Translate the last step here:

UNIT 3 – FASTER!

Say:

1. Often, I listen to music in the garden.

2. When I have time, I watch films in the living room.

3. I never have breakfast in the dining room.

4. Sometimes, I do my homework on the terrace.

5. Usually, I get dressed in my bedroom.

6. I always brush my teeth in the bathroom.

7. Every day, I watch TV in my brother's bedroom.

8. Twice a week, I prepare food in the kitchen.

9. At around 6:00 a.m., I do my homework in the games room.

10. When I have time, I read magazines in my parents' bedroom.

	Time	Mistakes	Referee's name
1			
2			
3			
4			

UNIT 3 – INFORMATION GAP TASK

Use these questions to find out the missing information from your partner. Answer the questions in the first person wherever you can: e.g. **"me meto en internet"**.

¿Con qué frecuencia _____? *How often _____?*	...te metes en internet? ...lees revistas? ...ves la tele? ...juegas a la Play? ...escuchas música? ...te lavas los dientes? ...preparas la comida?	*...do you go on the internet?* *...do you read magazines?* *...do you watch TV?* *...do you play on the PlayStation?* *...do you listen to music?* *...do you brush your teeth?* *...do you prepare food?*
¿Dónde _____? *Where _____?*		
¿Qué haces _____? *What do you do _____?*	...siempre? ...por lo general? ...a veces? ...siempre? ...todos los días? ...a menudo? ...en tu tiempo libre?	*...always?* *...usually?* *...sometimes?* *...always?* *...every day?* *...often?* *...in your free time?*

PARTNER 1

	Activity	How often	Location
José	Go on the internet		In the living room
Sandra		Often	
Paco	Listen to music		In my bedroom
Daniel	Brush teeth	Every day	
Sarah		Sometimes	In the kitchen

PARTNER 2

	Activity	How often	Location
José		Always	
Sandra	Play PlayStation		In the games room
Paco		Usually	
Daniel			In the bathroom
Sarah	Prepare food		

UNIT 3 – COMMUNICATIVE DRILLS

1	2	3
What do you do in your free time? - Sometimes, I watch TV in the living room. **How often do you do your homework?** - Every day.	**What do you do in your free time?** - When I have time, I prepare food in the kitchen. **How often do you play on the PlayStation?** - Twice a week, I play on the PlayStation in the games room.	**Where do you brush your teeth?** - Usually, I brush my teeth in the bathroom. And you? **Me too, but sometimes, I brush my teeth in the kitchen.** - Me too!
4	**5**	**6**
What do you do in your bedroom? - Often, I rest in my bedroom. When I have time, I read magazines. And you? **I never read magazines in my bedroom.**	**What do you do in your free time?** - I always go on the internet in my brother's bedroom. **How often do you do it?** - I go on the internet every day.	**How often do you prepare food?** - I never prepare food. And you? **I prepare food in the kitchen every day.** - Usually, I have breakfast in the kitchen.
7	**8**	**9**
Twice a week I chat with my mum on the terrace. And you? - I always chat with my mum in the living room. **Where do you read comics?** - I read comics in the garage.	**What do you do in your bedroom?** - I usually get dressed and I rest in my bedroom. What do you do in your free time? **I always listen to music in the dining room.**	**What do you do every day?** - Every day, I watch films in the games room. **Where do you play on the PlayStation?** - Often, I play on the PlayStation in the living room.

UNIT 3 – COMMUNICATIVE DRILLS
REFEREE CARD

1	2	3
¿Qué haces en tu tiempo libre? - A veces veo la tele en el salón. **¿Con qué frecuencia haces tus deberes?** - Todos los días.	**¿Qué haces en tu tiempo libre?** - Cuando tengo tiempo preparo comida en la cocina. **¿Con qué frecuencia juegas a la Play?** - Dos veces a la semana juego a la Play en la sala de juegos.	**¿Dónde te lavas los dientes?** - Por lo general, me lavo los dientes en el cuarto de baño. ¿Y tú? **Yo también, pero a veces me lavo los dientes en la cocina.** - ¡Yo también!

4	5	6
¿Qué haces en tu dormitorio? - A menudo descanso en mi dormitorio. Cuando tengo tiempo leo revistas. ¿Y tú? **Nunca leo revistas en mi dormitorio.**	**¿Qué haces en tu tiempo libre?** - Siempre me meto en internet en el dormitorio de mi hermano. **¿Con qué frecuencia lo haces?** Me meto en internet todos los días.	**¿Con qué frecuencia preparas comida?** - Nunca preparo comida. ¿Y tú? **Preparo comida en la cocina todos los días.** - Por lo general, desayuno en la cocina.

7	8	9
Dos veces a la semana charlo con mi madre en la terraza. ¿Y tú? - Siempre charlo con mi madre en el salón. **¿Dónde lees tebeos?** - Leo tebeos en el garaje.	**¿Qué haces en tu dormitorio?** - Por lo general, me visto y descanso en mi dormitorio. **¿Qué haces en tu tiempo libre?** - Siempre escucho música en el comedor.	**¿Qué haces todos los días?** - Todos los días veo películas en la sala de juegos. **¿Dónde juegas a la Play?** - A menudo juego a la Play en el salón.

UNIT 3 – SURVEY

	¿Cómo te llamas? *What is your name?*	¿Qué haces en tu tiempo libre? *What do you do in your free time?*	¿Con qué frecuencia escuchas música? *How often do you listen to music?*	¿Dónde haces los deberes? *Where do you do homework?*	¿Qué haces en el salón? *What do you do in the living room?*	¿Dónde desayunas? *Where do you have breakfast?*
e.g.	Me llamo Juan.	Cuando tengo tiempo veo películas en mi dormitorio.	Dos veces a la semana escucho música en la terraza.	A menudo hago mis deberes en el comedor.	Siempre leo revistas en el salón.	Por lo general, desayuno en la cocina.
1.						
2.						
3.						
4.						
5.						
6.						
7.						

UNIT 3 – ANSWERS

FIND SOMEONE WHO

Find someone who...		Name(s)
1.	...rests every day in the dining room.	Julia
2.	...plays on the PlayStation in the living room.	Nancy
3.	...watches television in the living room.	David
4.	...reads magazines on the terrace.	María/Felipe
5.	...uploads pics to Instagram.	Alejandro
6.	...usually watches films in the games room.	Amelia
7.	...rides their bike.	Pablo/Jorge
8.	...often prepares food in the kitchen.	Pepe
9.	...has breakfast in the kitchen at around 6:00 a.m.	Pedro/Marta
10.	...always goes on the internet in their bedroom.	Daniel
11.	...always chats with their mother in the garden.	James
12.	...usually watches series in the games room.	Juan
13.	...never watches television in the garage.	Catalina

STAIRCASE TRANSLATION

Todos los días veo la tele en el salón. Cuando tengo tiempo, escucho música en mi dormitorio. Dos veces a la semana subo fotos a Instagram en el jardín. Nunca monto en bici. ¿Qué haces en tu tiempo libre?

FASTER!

REFEREE SOLUTION:

1. A menudo escucho música en el jardín.   2. Cuando tengo tiempo veo películas en el salón.
3. Nunca desayuno en el comedor.   4. A veces hago mis deberes en la terraza.
5. Por lo general, me visto en mi dormitorio.   6. Siempre me lavo los dientes en el baño.
7. Todos los días veo la tele en el dormitorio de mi hermano.
8. Dos veces a la semana preparo comida en la cocina.
9. A eso de las seis de la mañana hago mis deberes en la sala de juegos.
10. Cuando tengo tiempo leo revistas en el dormitorio de mis padres.

INFORMATION GAP TASK

	Activity	How often	Location
José	Go on the internet	Always	In the living room
Sandra	Play on the PlayStation	Often	In the games room
Paco	Listen to music	Usually	In my bedroom
Daniel	Brush teeth	Every day	In the bathroom
Sarah	Prepare food	Sometimes	In the kitchen

UNIT 4. Talking about clothes & weather

¿Qué ropa llevas en casa?	What clothes do you wear at home?
¿Qué ropa llevas cuando hace frío/calor?	What clothes do you wear when it's cold/hot?
¿Qué ropa llevas cuando sales con tus amigos?	What do you wear when you go out with your friends?
Describe tu uniforme escolar	Describe your school uniform

Cuando *When*	**hace calor** *it's hot*		**llevo** *I wear*	**un abrigo** a coat	**amarillo** yellow	
	hace frío *it's cold*			**un bañador** a swimsuit	**blanco** white	
				un chaleco a waistcoat	**morado** purple	
				un chándal a tracksuit	**negro** black	
	juego al fútbol *I play football*			**un cinturón** a belt	**rojo** red	
				un collar a necklace		
	salgo con mi novio/novia *I go out with my boyfriend/girlfriend*			**un jersey** a jumper	***azul** blue	
				un reloj a watch	**gris** grey	
				un sombrero a hat	**marrón** brown	
				un traje a suit	**naranja** orange	
	salgo con mis amigos *I go out with my friends*			**un uniforme** a uniform	**rosa** pink	
				un vestido a dress	**verde** green	
	salgo con mis padres *I go out with my parents*			**una bufanda** a scarf		
				una camisa a shirt	**amarilla** yellow	
				una camiseta a t-shirt	**blanca** white	
				una camiseta sin mangas *tank top/vest*	**morada** purple	
				una chaqueta a jacket	**negra** black	
				una chaqueta deportiva *a sports jacket*	**roja** red	
				una corbata a tie		
				una falda a skirt		
			lleva *he/she wears*	**una gorra** a cap		
En casa At home				**botas** boots	**amarillos/as** yellow	
				calcetines socks	**azules** blue	
En la discoteca At the nightclub				**chanclas** flip-flops	**blancos/as** white	
En la playa At the beach				**pantalones** trousers	**dorados/as** golden	
				pantalones cortos shorts	**grises** grey	
				pantuflas slippers	**marrones** brown	
En el colegio At school				**pendientes** earrings	**morados/as** purple	
En el gimnasio At the gym				**sandalias** sandals	**naranjas** orange	
				vaqueros jeans	**negros/as** black	
Nunca Never				**zapatos** shoes	**rojos/as** red	
Por lo general Usually				**zapatos de tacón** *high-heeled shoes*	**verdes** green	
Siempre Always				**zapatillas (de deporte)** *trainers*		

*Author's note: The adjectives in this section (azul/gris/marrón/naranja/verde) stay the same regardless of the gender of the noun: e.g. Un traje verde / Una falda verde.

UNIT 4 – FIND SOMEONE WHO – Student Cards

Siempre llevo una gorra roja. **JULIA**	En la playa llevo un bañador blanco. **LUCÍA**	En el gimnasio llevo unas zapatillas de deporte azules. **FERNANDO**	Cuando hace frío llevo una bufanda roja. **AURORA**
Cuando salgo con mi novia llevo un traje azul. **MIGUEL**	En casa llevo unos pantalones cortos naranjas. **JUAN**	En el colegio llevo un uniforme marrón. **MÍA**	Cuando juego al fútbol llevo unas botas blancas. **MARTINA**
Cuando salgo con mis padres llevo un jersey negro. **LAURA**	Cuando hace frío llevo unos pantalones grises. **ELENA**	Nunca llevo una chaqueta verde. **JORGE**	En la discoteca llevo un cinturón amarillo. **JOSÉ**
Por lo general, llevo una corbata negra. **CARLA**	Cuando hace frío llevo una bufanda roja. **CARLOS**	Cuando hace calor llevo una camiseta blanca. **ANTONIO**	En casa llevo unos pantalones cortos naranjas. **ALBA**

UNIT 4 – FIND SOMEONE WHO – Student Grid

Qué ropa llevas?	*What clothes do you wear?*	
Find someone who...		**Name(s)**
1.	...wears a red scarf when it's cold.	
2.	...wears a white t-shirt when it's hot.	
3.	...wears orange shorts at home.	
4.	...wears white boots when playing football.	
5.	...wears a blue suit when going out with their girlfriend.	
6.	...wears grey trousers when it's cold.	
7.	...wears a brown uniform at school.	
8.	...never wears a green jacket.	
9.	...wears a yellow belt at the disco.	
10.	...wears a black jersey when going out with their parents.	
11.	...always wears a red cap.	
12.	...wears blue sports shoes in the gym.	
13.	...wears a white swimsuit at the beach.	

THE LANGUAGE GYM

UNIT 4 – ORAL PING-PONG – Person A

ENGLISH	SPANISH	ENGLISH	SPANISH
When it's cold, I wear a yellow coat.	Cuando hace frío llevo un abrigo amarillo.	When it's cold, I wear a pink scarf.	Cuando hace frío llevo una bufanda rosa.
At the beach, I wear a white swimsuit.		I always wear a red swimsuit.	
When I go out with my boyfriend, I wear an orange hat.	Cuando salgo con mi novio llevo un sombrero naranja.	When it's hot, I wear a green hat.	Cuando hace calor llevo un sombrero verde.
At the gym, I wear a green t-shirt.		At the gym, I wear an orange coat.	
When I go out with my girlfriend, I wear a black sleeveless shirt.	Cuando salgo con mi novia llevo una camiseta sin mangas negra.	At school, I wear a grey uniform.	En el colegio llevo un uniforme gris.
At home, I wear a blue shirt.		At the beach, I wear a black t-shirt.	
I never wear white jeans.	Nunca llevo vaqueros blancos.	When it's hot, I wear a yellow skirt.	Cuando hace calor llevo una falda amarilla.
When I go out with my friends, I wear green shorts.		At home, I wear red slippers.	
At the nightclub, I wear grey socks.	En la discoteca llevo calcetines grises.	At the nightclub, I wear orange shorts.	En la discoteca llevo pantalones cortos naranjas.
I always wear brown boots.		I always wear grey jeans.	

 **THE LANGUAGE GYM**

UNIT 4 – ORAL PING-PONG – Person B

ENGLISH	SPANISH	ENGLISH	SPANISH
When it's cold, I wear a yellow coat.		When it's cold, I wear a pink scarf.	
At the beach, I wear a white swimsuit.	En la playa llevo un bañador blanco.	I always wear a red swimsuit.	Siempre llevo un bañador rojo.
When I go out with my boyfriend, I wear an orange hat.		When it's hot, I wear a green hat.	
At the gym, I wear a green t-shirt.	En el gimnasio llevo una camiseta verde.	At the gym, I wear an orange coat.	En el gimnasio llevo un abrigo naranja.
When I go out with my girlfriend, I wear a black sleeveless shirt.		At school, I wear a grey uniform.	
At home, I wear a blue shirt.	En casa llevo una camisa azul.	At the beach, I wear a black t-shirt.	En la playa llevo una camiseta negra.
I never wear white jeans.		When it's hot, I wear a yellow skirt.	
When I go out with my friends, I wear green shorts.	Cuando salgo con mis amigos llevo pantalones cortos verdes.	At home, I wear red slippers.	En casa llevo pantuflas rojas.
At the nightclub, I wear grey socks.		At the nightclub, I wear orange shorts.	
I always wear brown boots.	Siempre llevo botas marrones.	I always wear grey jeans.	Siempre llevo vaqueros grises.

No Snakes No Ladders

7 When I go out with my girlfriend, I wear a white waistcoat.	**8** In school, she wears a blue skirt.	**23**	**24** When I play football, I wear black sports shoes.		
6 When I play football, I wear black shorts.	**9** Usually, he wears a golden necklace.	**22** When it's cold, I wear a grey coat.	**25** She never wears red boots.		
5 At school, I wear a red suit.	**10** I always wear a green watch.	**21** What clothes do you wear at home?	**26** What clothes do you wear when you go out with your friends?		
4 I never wear a black uniform.	**11** When I play football, I wear yellow socks.	**20** When I play football, I wear orange boots.	**27** What clothes do you wear when it's cold?		
3 When it's hot, he wears a blue watch.	**12** In the gym, he wears a red t-shirt.	**19** At the nightclub, I wear red trousers.	**28** When it's hot, she wears a white swimsuit.		
2 When I go out with my friends, I wear a brown dress.	**13** I always wear a red tie.	**18** In school, I wear white earrings.	**29** When I play football, I wear a green t-shirt.		
1 In the nightclub, she wears an orange necklace.	**14** When I go out with my parents, I wear brown shorts.	**17** Usually, I wear yellow socks.	**30** What clothes do you wear when it's hot?		
START	**15** When I go out with my friends, I wear orange sports shoes.	**16** I always wear green trousers.	**FINISH**		

No Snakes No Ladders

7 Cuando salgo con mi novia llevo un chaleco blanco.	**8** En el colegio **ella** lleva una falda azul.					**24** Cuando juego al fútbol llevo zapatillas de deporte negros.
6 Cuando juego al fútbol llevo pantalones cortos negros.	**9** Por lo general, **él** lleva un collar dorado.				**23** Siempre llevo un chaleco marrón.	
5 En el colegio llevo un traje rojo.	**10** Siempre llevo un reloj verde.			**22** Cuando hace frío llevo un abrigo gris.	**25** **Ella** nunca lleva botas rojas.	
4 Nunca llevo un uniforme negro.	**11** Cuando juego al fútbol llevo calcetines amarillos.		**21** ¿Qué ropa llevas en casa?	**26** ¿Qué ropa llevas cuando sales con tus amigos?		
3 Cuando hace calor **él** lleva un reloj azul.	**12** En el gimnasio **él** lleva una camiseta roja.	**20** Cuando juego al fútbol llevo botas naranjas.	**27** ¿Qué ropa llevas cuando hace frío?			
2 Cuando salgo con mis amigos llevo un vestido marrón.	**13** Siempre llevo una corbata roja.	**19** En la discoteca llevo pantalones rojos.	**28** Cuando hace calor **ella** lleva un bañador blanco.			
1 En la discoteca **ella** lleva un collar naranja.	**14** Cuando salgo con mis padres llevo pantalones cortos marrones.	**18** En el colegio llevo pendientes blancos.	**29** Cuando juego al fútbol llevo una camiseta verde.			
START	**15** Cuando salgo con mis amigos llevo zapatillas de deporte naranjas.	**16** Siempre llevo pantalones verdes.	**17** Por lo general, llevo calcetines amarillos.	**30** ¿Qué ropa llevas cuando hace calor?		**FINISH**

THE LANGUAGE GYM

44

UNIT 4 – STAIRCASE TRANSLATION

I always wear a blue coat and black trousers.

I always wear a blue coat and black trousers. When it's hot, I wear a white t-shirt...

I always wear a blue coat and black trousers. When it's hot, I wear a white t-shirt, red shorts and...

I always wear a blue coat and black trousers. When it's hot, I wear a white t-shirt, red shorts and a green hat. When I go out with my friends, I wear grey jeans...

I always wear a blue coat and black trousers. When it's hot, I wear a white t-shirt, red shorts and a green hat. When I go out with my friends, I wear grey jeans and a yellow shirt.

I always wear a blue coat and black trousers. When it's hot, I wear a white t-shirt, red shorts and a green hat. When I go out with my friends, I wear grey jeans and a yellow shirt. What do you wear when you go out with friends?

Translate the last step here:

UNIT 4 – FASTER!

Say:

1. I always wear a black watch.

2. I never wear a blue t-shirt.

3. When I go out with friends, I wear black jeans.

4. Usually, I wear a yellow dress.

5. At the gym, I wear a white tracksuit.

6. At home, I wear orange slippers.

7. When I go out with my parents, I wear a grey suit.

8. When I play football, I wear black boots.

9. At the nightclub, she wears a red jacket.

10. What clothes do you wear at home?

	Time	Mistakes	Referee's name
1			
2			
3			
4			

THE LANGUAGE GYM

UNIT 4 – THINGS IN COMMON

	1	2	3	4	5
¿Qué ropa llevas cuando hace calor?					
¿Qué ropa llevas cuando sales con tus amigos?					
¿Qué ropa llevas en casa?					
¿Qué ropa llevas en la discoteca?					
¿Qué ropa llevas en el gimnasio?					
¿Qué ropa llevas en la playa?					
¿Qué ropa llevas cuando sales con tus padres?					
¿Qué ropa llevas cuando hace frío?					
¿Llevas una corbata en el colegio?					

UNIT 4 – COMMUNICATIVE DRILLS

1	2	3
What clothes do you wear when it's cold? - When it's cold, I wear a red jumper. **What clothes do you wear when you go out with friends?** - I always wear a blue tracksuit.	**What clothes do you wear at home?** - At home, I wear a white t-shirt and blue jeans. **What clothes do you wear at the gym?** - Usually, I wear a white t-shirt and grey shorts.	**What clothes do you wear when it's hot?** - Usually, I wear a yellow swimsuit. **Describe your school uniform.** - At school, I wear a grey suit and a green tie.

4	5	6
What clothes do you wear when you go out with your boyfriend? - I wear a black skirt and a grey shirt. What clothes do you wear when you go out with your girlfriend? **When I go out with my girlfriend, I wear a blue suit.**	**Describe your school uniform.** - In school, I wear a brown jacket and blue trousers. **Do you wear a tie?** - Yes, I wear an orange tie and black shoes.	**When I go out with my friends I wear a yellow sports jacket. And you?** - I never wear a sports jacket. I always wear a red jumper with red high heel shoes.

7	8	9
What clothes do you wear when you play football? - I always wear blue boots and a black tracksuit. And you? **When I play football, I wear an orange vest and green trainers.**	**What clothes do you wear when you go out with your parents?** - I usually wear a white cap. **What clothes do you wear when it's cold?** - When it's cold, I wear a red coat.	**What clothes do you wear at the beach?** - At the beach, I wear a black swimsuit and a green hat. And you? **I usually wear a red cap and brown sandals.**

UNIT 4 – COMMUNICATIVE DRILLS
REFEREE CARD

1	2	3
¿Qué ropa llevas cuando hace frío? - Cuando hace frío llevo un jersey rojo. **¿Qué ropa llevas cuando sales con amigos?** - Siempre llevo un chándal azul.	**¿Qué ropa llevas en casa?** - En casa llevo una camiseta blanca y vaqueros azules. **¿Qué ropa llevas en el gimnasio?** - Por lo general, llevo una camiseta blanca y pantalones cortos grises.	**¿Qué ropa llevas cuando hace calor?** - Por lo general, llevo un bañador amarillo. **Describe tu uniforme escolar.** - En el colegio llevo un traje gris y una corbata verde.

4	5	6
¿Qué ropa llevas cuando sales con tu novio? - Llevo una falda negra y una camisa gris. ¿Qué ropa llevas cuando sales con tu novia? **Cuando salgo con mi novia llevo un traje azul.**	**Describe tu uniforme escolar.** - En el colegio llevo una chaqueta marrón y pantalones azules. **¿Llevas corbata?** - Sí, llevo una corbata naranja y zapatos negros.	**Cuando salgo con mis amigos llevo una chaqueta deportiva amarilla. ¿Y tú?** - Nunca llevo una chaqueta deportiva. Siempre llevo un jersey rojo con zapatos de tacón rojos.

7	8	9
¿Qué ropa llevas cuando juegas al fútbol? - Siempre llevo botas azules y un chándal negro. ¿Y tú? **Cuando juego al fútbol llevo una camiseta sin mangas naranja y zapatillas de deporte verdes.**	**¿Qué ropa llevas cuando sales con tus padres?** - Por lo general, llevo una gorra blanca. **¿Qué ropa llevas cuando hace frío?** - Cuando hace frío llevo un abrigo rojo.	**¿Qué ropa llevas en la playa?** - En la playa llevo un bañador negro y un sombrero verde. ¿Y tú? **Por lo general, llevo una gorra roja y sandalias marrones.**

UNIT 4 – SURVEY

	¿Cómo te llamas? *What is your name?*	¿Qué ropa llevas cuando hace calor? *What clothes do you wear when it's hot?*	¿Qué ropa llevas en casa? *What clothes do you wear at home?*	¿Qué ropa llevas cuando juegas al fútbol? *What clothes do you wear when you play football?*	¿Qué ropa llevas en el gimnasio? *What do you wear at the gym?*	¿Qué ropa llevas cuando sales con amigos? *What clothes do you wear when you go out with friends?*
e.g.	*Me llamo Juan.*	*Cuando hace calor llevo una camiseta blanca.*	*En casa llevo pantalones grises.*	*Siempre llevo botas negras.*	*En el gimnasio llevo un chándal azul.*	*Cuando salgo con los amigos llevo una chaqueta negra.*
1.						
2.						
3.						
4.						
5.						
6.						
7.						

THE LANGUAGE GYM

UNIT 4 – ANSWERS

FIND SOMEONE WHO

	Find someone who...	Name(s)
1.	...wears a red scarf when it's cold.	**Carlos/Aurora**
2.	...wears a white t-shirt when it's hot.	**Antonio**
3.	...wears orange shorts at home.	**Juan/Alba**
4.	...wears white boots when playing football.	**Martina**
5.	...wears a blue suit when going out with their girlfriend.	**Miguel**
6.	...wears trousers when it's cold.	**Elena**
7.	...wears a brown uniform at school.	**Mía**
8.	...never wears a green jacket.	**Jorge**
9.	...wears a yellow belt at the disco.	**José**
10.	...wears a black jersey when going out with their parents.	**Laura**
11.	...always wears a red cap.	**Julia**
12.	...wears blue sports shoes in the gym.	**Fernando**
13.	...wears a white swimsuit at the beach.	**Lucía**

STAIRCASE TRANSLATION

Siempre llevo un abrigo azul y pantalones negros. Cuando hace calor, llevo una camiseta blanca, pantalones cortos rojos y un sombrero verde. Cuando salgo con mis amigos, llevo vaqueros grises y una camisa amarilla. ¿Qué llevas cuando sales con amigos?

FASTER!

REFEREE SOLUTION:

1. Siempre llevo un reloj negro.   2. Nunca llevo una camiseta azul.
3. Cuando salgo con amigos llevo vaqueros negros.   4. Por lo general, llevo un vestido amarillo.
5. En el gimnasio llevo un chándal blanco.   6. En casa llevo pantuflas naranjas.
7. Cuando salgo con mis padres llevo un traje gris.   8. Cuando juego al fútbol llevo botas negras.
9. En la discoteca ella lleva una chaqueta roja.   10. ¿Qué ropa llevas en casa?

THINGS IN COMMON

Students give their own answers to the questions and make a note of which students they have things in common with.

UNIT 5.
My weekend plans – food & leisure

¿Qué vas a hacer este fin de semana?	What are you going to do this weekend?
¿Cómo crees que será?	What do you think it will be like?
¿Qué vas a tomar para el desayuno?	What are you going to have for breakfast?
¿Qué sueles comer para el almuerzo?	What do you usually eat for lunch?
¿Qué te gusta beber?	What do you like to drink?

Este fin de semana *This weekend* **El sábado/domingo que viene** *Next Saturday/Sunday* **Este sábado/domingo** *This Saturday/Sunday*	**voy a** *I am going* **mi familia y yo vamos a** *my family and I are going*	**hacer** *to do*	**deporte** **los deberes** **muchas cosas**	*sport* *homework* *many things*
		ir *to go*	**a un restaurante** **a un concierto** **al centro comercial** **de compras**	*to a restaurant* *to a concert* *to the mall* *shopping*
		jugar *to play*	**al fútbol** **a videojuegos**	*football* *videogames*
		tocar *to play (instrument)*	**el piano** **la guitarra**	*the piano* *the guitar*
		ver *to see*	**un partido** **una película** **una serie en Netflix**	*a match* *a film* *a series on Netflix*

Creo que será *I think it will be*	**bastante** *quite* **muy** *very* **un poco** *a bit*	**aburrido** *boring* **divertido** *fun* **emocionante** *exciting* **interesante** *interesting*
Creo que no será nada *It won't be … at all*		

Para el desayuno *For breakfast*	**me gusta** *I like* **suelo** *I usually* **voy a** *I am going (to)*	**comer** *to eat* **tomar** *to have*	**cereales con leche** **fruta** **jamón** **miel** **pescado** **pollo asado** **queso** **un bocadillo** **una ensalada** **una magdalena** **una tostada**	*cereal with milk* *fruit* *ham* *honey* *fish* *roast chicken* *cheese* *a sandwich* *a salad* *a cupcake* *a slice of toast*
Para el almuerzo *For lunch*				
Para la cena *For dinner*		**beber** *to drink* **tomar** *to have*	**agua** **café** **chocolate caliente** **un vaso de leche** **té** **zumo de naranja**	*water* *coffee* *hot chocolate* *a glass of milk* *tea* *orange juice*

THE LANGUAGE GYM

UNIT 5 – FIND SOMEONE WHO – Student Cards

Este fin de semana voy a ir a un restaurante. **ALBERTO**	El sábado que viene voy a hacer deporte. **FELIPE**	Este domingo mi familia y yo vamos a ir a un concierto. **JUANA**	Voy a ir al centro comercial con mi familia el domingo que viene. **BEATRIZ**
Para la cena voy a tomar pollo asado. **FRANCISCO**	Este sábado voy a hacer muchas cosas. **JUANITO**	El domingo que viene voy a ir de compras. **CATALINA**	Para el almuerzo suelo comer un bocadillo. **ANGELA**
Para la cena suelo comer pescado. **GIANFRANCO**	Este fin de semana voy a ver una serie en Netflix. **DANIELA**	Este fin de semana voy a tocar la guitarra. **EMILIA**	Este fin de semana voy a ir a un concierto. **OLIVIA**
El domingo que viene mi familia y yo vamos a ir al centro comercial. **GUILLERMO**	Para el desayuno voy a beber café. **LOUIS**	Este sábado voy a hacer muchas cosas. **DIANA**	El domingo que viene voy a jugar a videojuegos. **CARMEN**

UNIT 5 – FIND SOMEONE WHO – Student Grid

¿Qué vas a hacer este fin de semana?	*What are you going to do this weekend?*
¿Qué vas a tomar para el desayuno?	*What are you going to have for breakfast?*
¿Qué sueles comer para el almuerzo?	*What do you like to eat for lunch?*

	Find someone who...	Name(s)
1.	...is going to play videogames next Sunday.	
2.	...usually eats a sandwich for lunch.	
3.	...is going to go to a concert this Sunday.	
4.	...is going to have roast chicken for dinner.	
5.	...is going to go shopping next Sunday.	
6.	...is going to do many things this Saturday.	
7.	...is going to watch a series on Netflix this weekend.	
8.	...is going to drink coffee for breakfast.	
9.	...is going to play the guitar this weekend.	
10.	...is going to go to a restaurant this weekend.	
11.	...is going to do sport next Saturday.	
12.	...usually eats fish for dinner.	
13.	...is going to the mall with their family next Sunday.	

THE LANGUAGE GYM

52

UNIT 5 – ORAL PING-PONG – Person A

ENGLISH	SPANISH	ENGLISH	SPANISH
This weekend, I am going to go to the mall.	Este fin de semana voy a ir al centro comercial.	For breakfast, I am going to drink a glass of milk.	Para el desayuno voy a beber un vaso de leche.
Next Saturday, we are going to do sport.		For dinner, I usually have roast chicken.	
This Saturday, I am going to play the guitar.	Este sábado voy a tocar la guitarra.	For lunch, I like to drink water.	Para el almuerzo, me gusta beber agua.
This Sunday, we are going to watch a football match.		For breakfast, I usually eat fruit.	
This weekend, we are going to do many things.	Este fin de semana vamos a hacer muchas cosas.	This weekend, I am going to watch a series on Netflix.	Este fin de semana voy a ver una serie en Netflix.
I think it will be very fun.		For lunch, I like to drink water.	
For dinner, I am going to have fish.	Para la cena voy a tomar pescado.	This Sunday, we are going to go to the restaurant.	Este domingo vamos a ir al restaurante
Next Saturday, I am going to play videogames.		For dinner, I am going to have hot chocolate.	
This Saturday, I am going to do homework.	Este sábado voy a hacer los deberes.	I don't think it will be interesting at all.	Creo que no será nada interesante.
For lunch, I like to eat a salad.		For breakfast, I am going to drink tea.	

UNIT 5 – ORAL PING-PONG – Person B

ENGLISH	SPANISH	ENGLISH	SPANISH
This weekend, I am going to go to the mall.		For breakfast, I am going to drink a glass of milk.	
Next Saturday, we are going to do sport.	El sábado que viene vamos a hacer deporte.	For dinner, I usually have roast chicken.	Para la cena suelo comer pollo asado.
This Saturday, I am going to play the guitar.		For lunch, I like to drink water.	
This Sunday, we are going to watch a football match.	Este domingo vamos a ver un partido de fútbol.	For breakfast, I usually eat fruit.	Para el desayuno suelo comer fruta.
This weekend, we are going to do many things.		This weekend, I am going to watch a series on Netflix.	
I think it will be very fun.	Creo que será muy divertido.	For lunch, I like to drink water.	Para el almuerzo me gusta beber agua.
For dinner, I am going to have fish.		This Sunday, we are going to go to the restaurant.	
Next Saturday, I am going to play videogames.	El sábado que viene voy a jugar a videojuegos.	For dinner, I am going to have hot chocolate.	Para la cena voy a tomar chocolate caliente.
This Saturday, I am going to do homework.		I don't think it will be interesting at all.	
For lunch, I like to eat a salad.	Para el almuerzo me gusta comer una ensalada.	For breakfast, I am going to drink tea.	Para el desayuno voy a beber té.

No Snakes No Ladders

7 I think it will be very fun.

8 What are you going to do this weekend?

23 For breakfast, I am going to drink a glass of milk.

24 For breakfast, I am going to have coffee.

6 For breakfast, I usually eat fruit.

9 For lunch, I like to eat ham.

22 How do you think it will be?

25 This Saturday, we are going to go shopping at the mall.

5 For dinner, I usually eat roast chicken.

10 For dinner, I am going to have fish.

21 This Sunday, we are going to watch a football match.

26 This Sunday we are going to go to a concert.

4 For breakfast, I am going to drink tea.

11 This Saturday, I am going to do homework.

20 For lunch, I usually eat a sandwich.

27 For dinner, I am going to eat a slice of toast.

3 For dinner, I am going to have hot chocolate.

12 This weekend, we are going to do many things.

19 What are you going to have for breakfast?

28 What do you usually eat for lunch?

2 For lunch, I like to drink water.

13 This weekend, I am going to watch a series on Netflix.

18 This Saturday, I am going to play the guitar.

29 What do you like to drink?

1 For lunch, I like to eat a salad.

14 Next Saturday, we are going to do sport.

17 This Sunday, we are going to go to the restaurant.

30 This Saturday we are going to play the piano.

START

15 This weekend, we are going to go to the mall.

16 Next Saturday, I am going to play videogames.

FINISH

THE LANGUAGE GYM

No Snakes No Ladders

	1 Para el almuerzo me gusta comer una ensalada.	**2** Para el almuerzo me gusta beber agua.	**3** Para la cena voy a tomar chocolate caliente.	**4** Para el desayuno voy a beber té.	**5** Para la cena suelo comer pollo asado.	**6** Para el desayuno suelo comer fruta.	**7** Creo que será muy divertido.
SALIDA	**14** El sábado que viene vamos a hacer deporte.	**13** Este fin de semana voy a ver una serie en Netflix.	**12** Este fin de semana vamos a hacer muchas cosas.	**11** Este sábado voy a hacer los deberes.	**10** Para la cena voy a tomar pescado.	**9** Para el almuerzo me gusta comer jamón.	**8** ¿Qué vas a hacer este fin de semana?
15 Este fin de semana vamos a ir al centro comercial.	**16** El sábado que viene voy a jugar a videojuegos.	**17** Este domingo vamos a ir al restaurante.	**18** Este sábado voy a tocar la guitarra.	**19** ¿Qué vas a tomar para el desayuno?	**20** Para el almuerzo suelo comer un bocadillo.	**21** Este domingo vamos a ver un partido de fútbol.	**22** ¿Cómo crees que será?	**23** Para el desayuno voy a beber un vaso de leche.
LLEGADA	**30** Este sábado vamos a tocar el piano.	**29** ¿Qué te gusta beber?	**28** ¿Qué sueles comer para el almuerzo?	**27** Para la cena voy a comer una tostada.	**26** Este domingo vamos a ir a un concierto.	**25** Este sábado vamos a ir de compras al centro comercial.	**24** Para el desayuno voy a tomar café.

THE LANGUAGE GYM

56

UNIT 5 – STAIRCASE TRANSLATION

This weekend...

This weekend, I'm going to go to a restaurant.

This weekend, I'm going to go to a restaurant. I think it will be very fun.

This weekend, I'm going to go to a restaurant. I think it will be very fun. For dinner, I like to eat...

This weekend, I'm going to go to a restaurant. I think it will be very fun. For dinner, I like to eat roast chicken and a salad.

This weekend, I'm going to go to a restaurant. I think it will be very fun. For dinner, I like to eat roast chicken and a salad. Next Sunday, my family and I are going to go shopping.

Translate the last step here:

UNIT 5 – FASTER!

Say:

1. What are you going to do this weekend?

2. This weekend, I'm going to go shopping.

3. This Saturday, I'm going to play videogames.

4. What do you like to drink?

5. For breakfast, I usually drink coffee.

6. For lunch, I like to eat a sandwich.

7. I think it will be quite fun.

8. Next Sunday, my family and I are going to go to a concert.

	Time	Mistakes	Referee's name
1			
2			
3			
4			

UNIT 5 – FAST & FURIOUS
(Fill in the missing verbs)

ROUND 1

1. Este sábado vamos a _____ al centro comercial.
2. Este fin de semana voy a _____ deporte.
3. El domingo que viene vamos a _____ un partido de fútbol.
4. Este fin de semana voy a _____ la guitarra.
5. Este sábado mi familia y yo vamos a _____ a un restaurante.
6. Este domingo vamos a _____ una serie en Netflix.
7. Voy a _____ muchos deberes este sábado.
8. Este sábado voy a _____ al fútbol.
9. El domingo que viene mi familia y yo vamos a _____ de compras.
10. Este fin de semana vamos a _____ a un concierto.

	Time 1	Time 2	Time 3	Time 4
Time				
Mistakes				

ROUND 2

1. Este fin de semana voy a _____ de compras.
2. El sábado que viene vamos a _____ al fútbol.
3. Este sábado vamos a _____ un partido de fútbol.
4. Este fin de semana mi familia y yo vamos a _____ muchas cosas.
5. Este domingo voy a _____ la guitarra.
6. Este fin de semana voy a _____ una serie en Netflix.
7. Este sábado voy a _____ los deberes.
8. Mi familia y yo vamos a _____ a un restaurante.
9. Este fin de semana vamos a _____ deporte.
10. El domingo que viene vamos a _____ de compras.

	Time 1	Time 2	Time 3	Time 4
Time				
Mistakes				

UNIT 5 – COMMUNICATIVE DRILLS

1	2	3
What are you going to do this weekend? - This weekend, I'm going to play guitar. **What do you think it will be like?** - I think it will be very fun.	**What do you have for breakfast?** - For breakfast, I like to have fruit. And you? **I usually eat cereal with milk. For dinner, I'm going to eat roast chicken!**	**What do you usually eat for lunch?** - For lunch, I usually eat a sandwich and a salad. **What do you like to drink?** -I like to drink tea and coffee.

4	5	6
What do you like to have for dinner? - For dinner, I like to have fish or ham. **What do you like to drink?** - For breakfast I like to drink a glass of milk.	**What are you going to do this weekend?** - This Saturday, I'm going to go shopping. **And Sunday?** -This Sunday, my family and I are going to play videogames.	**What are you going to do this Sunday?** - This Sunday, I'm going to go to a concert. And you? **My family and I are going to play football.**

7	8	9
What are you going to have for dinner? - For dinner, I am going to eat a sandwich and a cupcake. **What are you going to drink?** - I usually drink orange juice.	**What are you going to do next Saturday?** - Next Saturday, I'm going to do many things. And you? **I'm going to do sport. I think it will be very fun!**	**What do you usually have for lunch?** - For lunch, I usually have cheese and ham. This weekend, I'm going to eat a slice of toast and honey. **I like honey. I'm going to eat fruit and salad.**

UNIT 5 – COMMUNICATIVE DRILLS
REFEREE CARD

1	2	3
¿Qué vas a hacer este fin de semana? - Este fin de semana voy a tocar la guitarra. ¿Cómo crees que será? - Creo que será muy divertido.	¿Qué sueles tomar para el desayuno? - Para el desayuno me gusta tomar fruta. ¿Y tú? **Suelo comer cereales con leche. ¡Para la cena voy a comer pollo asado!**	¿Qué sueles comer para el almuerzo? - Para el almuerzo suelo comer un bocadillo y una ensalada. ¿Qué te gusta beber? - Me gusta beber té y café.

4	5	6
¿Qué te gusta tomar para la cena? - Para la cena me gusta tomar pescado o jamón. ¿Qué te gusta beber? - Para el desayuno me gusta beber un vaso de leche.	¿Qué vas a hacer este fin de semana? - Este sábado voy a ir de compras. ¿Y el domingo? - Este domingo mi familia y yo vamos a jugar a videojuegos.	¿Qué vas a hacer este domingo? - Este domingo voy a ir a un concierto. ¿Y tú? **Mi familia y yo vamos a jugar al fútbol.**

7	8	9
¿Qué vas a comer para la cena? - Para la cena voy a comer un bocadillo y una magdalena. ¿Qué vas a beber? Suelo beber zumo de naranja.	¿Qué vas a hacer el sábado que viene? - El sábado que viene voy a hacer muchas cosas. ¿Y tú? **Voy a hacer deporte. ¡Creo que será muy divertido!**	¿Qué sueles tomar para el almuerzo? - Para el almuerzo suelo tomar queso y jamón. Este fin de semana voy a comer una tostada y miel. **Me gusta la miel. Voy a comer fruta y ensalada.**

UNIT 5 – SURVEY

	¿Cómo te llamas? *What is your name?*	¿Qué vas a hacer este fin de semana? *What are you going to do this weekend?*	¿Qué sueles tomar para el desayuno? *What do you usually have for breakfast?*	¿Qué te gusta beber? *What do you like to drink?*	¿Qué sueles comer para el almuerzo? *What do you usually eat for lunch?*	¿Qué vas a comer para la cena? *What are you going to eat for dinner?*
e.g.	Me llamo Juan.	Este fin de semana voy a ir a un restaurante.	Para el desayuno suelo tomar una tostada.	Me gusta beber café.	Para el almuerzo me gusta comer una ensalada.	Para la cena voy a comer pescado.
1.						
2.						
3.						
4.						
5.						
6.						
7.						

UNIT 5 – ANSWERS

FIND SOMEONE WHO

Find someone who...		Name(s)
1.	...is going to play videogames next Sunday.	**Carmen**
2.	...usually eats a sandwich for lunch.	**Angela**
3.	...is going to go to a concert this Sunday.	**Juana/Olivia**
4.	...is going to have roast chicken for dinner.	**Francisco**
5.	...is going to go shopping next Sunday.	**Catalina**
6.	...is going to do many things this Saturday.	**Juanito/Diana**
7.	...is going to watch a series on Netflix this weekend.	**Daniela**
8.	...is going to drink coffee for breakfast.	**Louis**
9.	...is going to play the guitar this weekend.	**Emilia**
10.	...is going to go to a restaurant this weekend.	**Alberto**
11.	...is going to do sport next Saturday.	**Felipe**
12.	...usually eats fish for dinner.	**Gianfranco**
13.	...is going to the mall with their family next Sunday.	**Beatriz/Guillermo**

STAIRCASE TRANSLATION

Este fin de semana voy a ir a un restaurante. Creo que será muy divertido. Para la cena, me gusta comer pollo asado y una ensalada. El domingo que viene, mi familia y yo vamos a ir de compras.

FASTER! REFEREE SOLUTION:

1. ¿Qué vas a hacer este fin de semana?   2. Este fin de semana voy a ir de compras.
3. Este sábado voy a jugar a videojuegos.   4. ¿Qué te gusta beber?   5. Para el desayuno suelo beber café.
6. Para el almuerzo me gusta comer un bocadillo.   7. Creo que será bastante divertido.
8. El domingo que viene, mi familia y yo vamos a ir a un concierto.

FAST & FURIOUS

ROUND 1
1. Este sábado vamos a **ir** al centro comercial.   2. Este fin de semana voy a **hacer** deporte.
3. El domingo que viene vamos a **ver** un partido de fútbol.   4. Este fin de semana voy a **tocar** la guitarra.
5. Este sábado mi familia y yo vamos a **ir** a un restaurante.   6. Este domingo vamos a **ver** una serie en Netflix.
7. Voy a **hacer** muchos deberes este sábado.   8. Este sábado voy a **jugar** al fútbol.
9. El domingo que viene mi familia y yo vamos a **ir** de compras.
10. Este fin de semana vamos a **ir** a un concierto.

ROUND 2
1. Este fin de semana voy a **ir** de compras.   2. El sábado que viene vamos a **jugar** al fútbol.
3. Este sábado vamos a **ver** un partido de fútbol.
4. Este fin de semana mi familia y yo vamos a **hacer** muchas cosas.   5. Este domingo voy a **tocar** la guitarra.
6. Este fin de semana voy a **ver** una serie en Netflix.   7. Este sábado voy a **hacer** los deberes.
8. Mi familia y yo vamos a **ir** a un restaurante.   9. Este fin de semana vamos a **hacer** deporte
10. El domingo que viene vamos a **ir** de compras.

 **THE LANGUAGE GYM**

UNIT 6. Saying where I live

¿Dónde vives?	Where do you live?
¿Qué hay en tu ciudad?	What is there in your city?
¿Te gusta tu barrio? ¿Por qué?	Do you like your neighbourhood? Why?

Vivo en *I live in* **Vivimos en** *We live in*	**Berlín** **Cardiff** **Dublín** **Edimburgo** **Londres** **Madrid** **Niza** **París** **Roma**	**Está en** *It is in*	**el centro de** **el norte de** **el este de** **el sur de** **el oeste de** **el noroeste de** **el sureste de**	**Alemania** **Canadá** **Escocia** **España** **Francia** **Gales** **Inglaterra** **Irlanda** **Italia**

Cerca de mi casa *Near my house* **En el centro** *In the centre* **En mi barrio** *In my neighbourhood* **En mi calle** *On my street* **En mi ciudad** *In my city*	**hay** *there is/are* **no hay** *there isn't / aren't*	**cafeterías** *cafés* **restaurantes** *restaurants* **una calle peatonal** *a pedestrian street*	**un acuario** **un centro comercial** **un cine** **un club juvenil** **un parque** **una pista de patinaje** **un polideportivo** **un jardín botánico**	*an aquarium* *a shopping mall* *a cinema* *a youth club* *a park* *a skating rink* *a sports centre* *a botanical garden*
		muchas cosas que hacer **muchas cosas que ver** **mucho que hacer para los jóvenes** **muchos jóvenes**	*many things to do* *many things to see* *a lot to do for young people* *lots of young people*	
	tenemos *we have* **no tenemos** *we do not have*	**muchas** *many (f – pl.)*	**áreas verdes** **calles bonitas** **instalaciones deportivas** **tiendas**	*green areas* *beautiful streets* *sports facilities* *shops*
		muchos *many (m – pl.)*	**edificios antiguos** **restaurantes**	*old buildings* *restaurants*

(No) Me gusta mi barrio porque *I (don't) like my neighbourhood because*	***es** it is*	**peligroso** **seguro**	*dangerous* *safe*
	está *it is*	**bien/mal cuidado** **limpio** **sucio**	*well/badly looked after* *clean* *dirty*
	(no) hay *there is (not)*	**mucha contaminación** **mucho ruido** **mucho tráfico**	*a lot of pollution* *a lot of noise* *a lot of traffic*
	(no) se puede *one can (not)*	**comer bien** **hacer deporte** **pasear**	*eat well* *do sport* *go for a walk*

*Author's note: "es" and "está" are used for different things. "Es" comes from **SER** and refers to physical and character descriptions. "Está" comes from **ESTAR** and is used to describe states and conditions. You will practice them in context in this unit. For a full explanation and practice exercises check out the matching unit in our **Spanish Verb Pivots** grammar book.

UNIT 6 – FIND SOMEONE WHO – Student Cards

En el centro de la ciudad hay un polideportivo. **PEDRO**	En mi calle hay un club juvenil. **ALEJANDRO**	En mi ciudad no tenemos un acuario. **MARTA**	En el centro de mi barrio hay una calle peatonal. **PATRICIA**
Muy cerca de mi casa hay un cine moderno. **RAMONA**	Hay muchas cosas que hacer en mi barrio. **PACO**	En mi barrio tenemos un polideportivo. **JAIME**	En mi calle hay muchos restaurantes. **MIKEL**
En mi barrio hay muchas cosas que hacer. **CARLA**	Cerca de mi casa hay un parque. **RAFAEL**	En el centro de la ciudad hay un polideportivo. **JAVIER**	Cerca de mi casa hay un cine. **ANDREA**
No hay un acuario en mi ciudad. **PEPA**	En mi ciudad tenemos un centro comercial. **DOLORES**	En mi ciudad tenemos una pista de patinaje. **BRUNO**	En mi barrio tenemos muchos edificios antiguos. **LIONEL**

UNIT 6 – FIND SOMEONE WHO – Student Grid

¿Dónde vives? ¿Qué hay en tu ciudad?	*Where do you live?* *What is there in your city?*	
Find someone who...		**Name(s)**
1.	...has a pedestrian street in the centre of their neighbourhood.	
2.	...has a shopping centre in their city.	
3.	...has lots of old buildings in their neighbourhood.	
4.	...has many things to do in their neighbourhood.	
5.	...has lots of restaurants on their street.	
6.	...has a sports centre in the city centre.	
7.	...has a youth club on their street.	
8.	...doesn't have an aquarium in their city.	
9.	...lives near a park.	
10.	...lives near a cinema.	
11.	...has a sports centre in their neighbourhood.	
12.	...is a red herring. 🐟 (no match)	

UNIT 6 – ORAL PING-PONG – Person A

ENGLISH	SPANISH	ENGLISH	SPANISH
I live in Berlin. It's in the east of Germany.	Vivo en Berlín. Está en el este de Alemania.	I like my neighbourhood because one can do sport.	Me gusta mi barrio porque se puede hacer deporte.
We live in Cardiff. It's in the south of Wales.		I don't like my neighbourhood because there is a lot of pollution.	
In my city, there are many things to do.	En mi ciudad hay muchas cosas que hacer.	I live in Rome. It's in the west of Italy.	Vivo en Roma. Está en el oeste de Italia.
In the centre of my neighbourhood, there is a pedestrian street.		In my city, we don't have an aquarium.	
On my street, there aren't many young people.	En mi calle no hay muchos jóvenes.	In my city, we have many restaurants.	En mi ciudad tenemos muchos restaurantes.
I don't like my neighbourhood because it's dangerous.		I live in Paris. It's in the north of France.	
I like my neighbourhood because it's clean.	Me gusta mi barrio porque está limpio.	Near my house, there is a park.	Cerca de mi casa hay un parque.
I don't like my neighbourhood because there is a lot of noise.		I like my neighbourhood because one can go for a walk.	
I live in Madrid. It's in the centre of Spain.	Vivo en Madrid. Está en el centro de España.	In my city, we have a cinema.	En mi ciudad tenemos un cine.
We live in Edinburgh. It's in the north of Scotland.		I live in London. It's in the south east of England.	

UNIT 6 – ORAL PING-PONG – Person B

ENGLISH	SPANISH	ENGLISH	SPANISH
I live in Berlin. It's in the east of Germany.		I like my neighbourhood because one can do sport.	
We live in Cardiff. It's in the south of Wales.	Vivimos en Cardiff. Está en el sur de Gales.	I don't like my neighbourhood because there is a lot of pollution.	No me gusta mi barrio porque hay mucha contaminación.
In my city, there are many things to do.		I live in Rome. It's in the west of Italy.	
In the centre of my neighbourhood, there is a pedestrian street.	En el centro de mi barrio hay una calle peatonal.	In my city, we don't have an aquarium.	En mi ciudad no tenemos un acuario.
On my street, there aren't many young people.		In my city, we have many restaurants.	
I don't like my neighbourhood because it's dangerous.	No me gusta mi barrio porque es peligroso.	I live in Paris. It's in the north of France.	Vivo en París. Está en el norte de Francia.
I like my neighbourhood because it's clean.		Near my house, there is a park.	
I don't like my neighbourhood because there is a lot of noise.	No me gusta mi barrio porque hay mucho ruido.	I like my neighbourhood because one can go for a walk.	Me gusta mi barrio porque se puede pasear.
I live in Madrid. It's in the centre of Spain.		In my city, we have a cinema.	
We live in Edinburgh. It's in the north of Scotland.	Vivimos en Edimburgo. Está en el norte de Escocia.	I live in London. It's in the south east of England.	Vivo en Londres. Está en el sureste de Inglaterra.

No Snakes No Ladders

	7 I like my neighbourhood because there isn't much noise.	**6** Where do you live?	**5** Near my house, there is a botanical garden.	**4** In my city, there is a lot of traffic.	**3** In my neighbourhood there are lots of shops.	**2** I live in Berlin. It is in the east of Germany.	**1** We live in Cardiff. It is in the south of Wales.
	8 I don't like my neighbourhood because it's dangerous.	**9** In my city, we don't have a shopping centre.	**10** In my city, we have many shops.	**11** What is there in your city?	**12** I don't like my neighbourhood because there is a lot of pollution.	**13** I like my neighbourhood because one can do sport.	**14** I live in Rome. It's in the west of Italy.
	23 Are there old buildings?	**22** I don't like my neighbourhood because one can't do sport.	**21** I live in Paris. It's in the north of France.	**20** We live in Edinburgh. It's in the south of Scotland.	**19** I like my neighbourhood because there isn't much noise.	**18** I like my neighbourhood because it's clean.	**17** Is there a lot of traffic in your city?
	24 I live in London. It's very dirty.	**25** In my city, there is a lot of noise.	**26** Do you like your neighbourhood? Why?	**27** I like my neighbourhood because one can go for a walk.	**28** I live in Madrid. It's in the centre of Spain.	**29** In my city we have an aquarium.	**30** What can you do in your neighbourhood?

START

15 I live in London. It's in the south east of England.

16 On my street, there aren't many old buildings.

FINISH

THE LANGUAGE GYM

No Snakes No Ladders

7 Me gusta mi barrio porque no hay mucho ruido.	**6** ¿Dónde vives?	**5** Cerca de mi casa hay un jardín botánico.	**4** En mi ciudad hay mucho tráfico.	**3** En mi barrio hay muchas tiendas.	**2** Vivo en Berlín. Está en el este de Alemania.	**1** Vivimos en Cardiff. Está en el sur de Gales.
8 No me gusta mi barrio porque es peligroso.	**9** En mi ciudad no tenemos un centro comercial.	**10** En mi ciudad tenemos muchas tiendas.	**11** ¿Qué hay en tu ciudad?	**12** No me gusta mi barrio porque hay mucha contaminación.	**13** Me gusta mi barrio porque se puede hacer deporte.	**14** Vivo en Roma. Está en el oeste de Italia.
23 ¿Hay edificios antiguos?	**22** No me gusta mi barrio porque no se puede hacer deporte.	**21** Vivo en París. Está en el norte de Francia.	**20** Vivimos en Edimburgo. Está en el sur de Escocia.	**19** Me gusta mi barrio porque no hay mucho ruido.	**18** Me gusta mi barrio porque está limpio.	**17** ¿Hay mucho tráfico en tu ciudad?
24 Vivo en Londres. Está muy sucio.	**25** En mi ciudad hay mucho ruido.	**26** ¿Te gusta tu barrio? ¿Por qué?	**27** Me gusta mi barrio porque se puede pasear.	**28** Vivo en Madrid. Está en el centro de España.	**29** En mi ciudad tenemos un acuario.	**30** ¿Qué se puede hacer en tu barrio?

SALIDA

15 Vivo en Londres. Está en el sureste de Inglaterra.

16 En mi calle no hay muchos edificios antiguos.

LLEGADA

THE LANGUAGE GYM

UNIT 6 – STAIRCASE TRANSLATION

I live in London. It is in the south east of England.

I live in London. It is in the south east of England. In my neighbourhood, there are many things to do.

I live in London. It is in the south east of England. In my neighbourhood, there are many things to do. I like my neighbourhood because it is clean.

I live in London. It is in the south east of England. In my neighbourhood, there are many things to do. I like my neighbourhood because it is clean. On my street, there is a park.

I live in London. It is in the south east of England. In my neighbourhood, there are many things to do. I like my neighbourhood because it is clean. On my street, there is a park. In the centre there is a cinema and lots of shops.

I live in London. It is in the south east of England. In my neighbourhood, there are many things to do. I like my neighbourhood because it is clean. On my street, there is a park. In the centre, there is a cinema and lots of shops. I like my city because there isn't a lot of traffic.

Translate the last step here:

UNIT 6 – FASTER!

Say:

1. Where do you live?

2. I live in Madrid. It is in the centre of Spain.

3. Near my house, there are restaurants.

4. I like my city because it is safe.

5. What is there in your city?

6. In the centre, there is a sports centre.

7. We live in Cardiff. It is in the south of Wales.

8. I like my neighbourhood because one can eat well.

9. In my city, we have many old buildings.

10. Do you like your street?

	Time	Mistakes	Referee's name
1			
2			
3			
4			

UNIT 6 – TRAPDOOR

Cerca de mi casa En mi ciudad En el centro En mi barrio En mi calle	hay no hay tenemos no tenemos	cafeterías muchos jóvenes restaurantes un acuario un centro comercial un cine un club juvenil un jardín botánico un polideportivo un parque una calle peatonal una pista de patinaje

1. In my city, we have many restaurants.
2. Near my house, there is a park.
3. In my neighbourhood, there isn't an aquarium.
4. In the centre, there is a cinema.
5. On my street, there aren't many young people.
6. In my city, we have a sports centre.
7. In my neighbourhood, there is a pedestrian street.

	Time 1	Time 2	Time 3	Time 4
Time				
Mistakes				

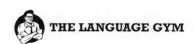 **THE LANGUAGE GYM**

UNIT 6 – COMMUNICATIVE DRILLS

1	2	3
Do you like your city? Why? - I like my city because there is a youth club. **Where do you live?** - I live in Berlin.	**Do you like your neighbourhood? Why?** - I don't like my neighbourhood because there is a lot of pollution. **What is there in your neighbourhood?** - In my neighbourhood, we have many sports facilities.	**What is there on your street?** - On my street, there aren't many things to do. **Do you like your neighbourhood? Why?** - Yes, I like my neighbourhood because it is safe.
4	**5**	**6**
Do you like your street? Why? - I like my street because it's clean. **Where do you live?** - I live in Madrid. It's in the centre of Spain.	**What is near your house?** - Near my house, there are many cafés. **Where do you live?** - We live in London. It's in the south east of England.	**Where do you live?** - I live in Rome. **Do you like your city? Why?** - Yes, I like my city because there are many shops.
7	**8**	**9**
Do you like your neighbourhood? Why? - I don't like my neighbourhood because there's a lot of noise. **What is there in your city?** - In my city, there are many shops.	**Where do you live?** - We live in Cardiff. It's in the south of Wales. **What is there in the centre?** - In the centre, there's a park.	**Where do you live?** - I live in Madrid. I really like my city. Where do you live? **I live in London. What is there in your city?** - In my city, we have many beautiful streets.

UNIT 6 – COMMUNICATIVE DRILLS
REFEREE CARD

1	2	3
¿Te gusta tu ciudad? ¿Por qué? - Me gusta mi ciudad porque hay un club juvenil. **¿Dónde vives?** - Vivo en Berlín.	**¿Te gusta tu barrio? ¿Por qué?** - No me gusta mi barrio porque hay mucha contaminación. **¿Qué hay en tu barrio?** - En mi barrio tenemos muchas instalaciones deportivas.	**¿Qué hay en tu calle?** - En mi calle no hay muchas cosas que hacer. **¿Te gusta tu barrio? ¿Por qué?** - Sí, me gusta mi barrio porque es seguro.

4	5	6
¿Te gusta tu calle? ¿Por qué? - Me gusta mi calle porque está limpia. **¿Dónde vives?** - Vivo en Madrid. Está en el centro de España.	**¿Qué hay cerca de tu casa?** - Cerca de mi casa hay muchas cafeterías. **¿Dónde vives?** - Vivimos en Londres. Está en el sureste de Inglaterra.	**¿Dónde vives?** - Vivo en Roma. **¿Te gusta tu ciudad? ¿Por qué?** - Sí, me gusta mi ciudad porque hay muchas tiendas.

7	8	9
¿Te gusta tu barrio? ¿Por qué? - No me gusta mi barrio porque hay mucho ruido. **¿Qué hay en tu ciudad?** - En mi ciudad hay muchas tiendas.	**¿Dónde vives?** - Vivimos en Cardiff. Está en el sur de Gales. **¿Qué hay en el centro?** - En el centro hay un parque.	**¿Dónde vives?** - Vivo en Madrid. Me gusta mucho mi ciudad. ¿Dónde vives? **Vivo en Londres. ¿Qué hay en tu ciudad?** - En mi ciudad tenemos muchas calles bonitas.

UNIT 6 – SURVEY

	¿Cómo te llamas? *What is your name?*	¿Dónde vives? *Where do you live?*	¿Qué hay en tu ciudad? *What is there in your city?*	¿Te gusta tu barrio? *Do you like your neighbourhood?*	¿Qué hay en tu calle? *What is there on your street?*	¿Qué hay en el centro? *What is there in the centre?*
e.g.	*Me llamo Juan.*	*Vivo en Cardiff. Está en el sur de Gales.*	*En mi ciudad hay un jardín botánico.*	*No me gusta mi barrio porque está sucio.*	*En mi calle tenemos muchas tiendas.*	*En el centro hay un cine y un parque.*
1.						
2.						
3.						
4.						
5.						
6.						
7.						

UNIT 6 – ANSWERS

FIND SOMEONE WHO

Find someone who...		Name(s)
1.	...has a pedestrian street in the centre of their neighbourhood.	**Patricia**
2.	...has a shopping centre in their city.	**Dolores**
3.	...has lots of old buildings in their neighbourhood.	**Lionel**
4.	...has many things to do in their neighbourhood.	**Paco/Carla**
5.	...has lots of restaurants on their street.	**Mikel**
6.	...has a sports centre in the city centre.	**Pedro/Javier**
7.	...has a youth club on their street.	**Alejandro**
8.	...doesn't have an aquarium in their city.	**Marta/Pepa**
9.	...lives near a park.	**Rafael**
10.	...lives near a cinema.	**Ramona/Andrea**
11.	...has a sports centre in their neighbourhood.	**Jaime**
12.	...is a red herring. 🐟 (no match)	**Bruno**

STAIRCASE TRANSLATION

Vivo en Londres. Está en el sureste de Inglaterra. En mi barrio hay muchas cosas que hacer. Me gusta mi barrio porque está limpio. En mi calle hay un parque. En el centro hay un cine y muchas tiendas. Me gusta mi ciudad porque no hay mucho tráfico.

FASTER!

REFEREE SOLUTION:

1. ¿Dónde vives?   2. Vivo en Madrid. Está en el centro de España.   3. Cerca de mi casa hay restaurantes.
4. Me gusta mi ciudad porque es segura.   5. ¿Qué hay en tu ciudad?   6. En el centro hay un polideportivo.
7. Vivimos en Cardiff. Está en el sur de Gales.   8. Me gusta mi barrio porque se puede comer bien.
9. En mi ciudad tenemos muchos edificios antiguos.   10. ¿Te gusta tu calle?

TRAPDOOR

1. En mi ciudad tenemos muchos restaurantes.   2. Cerca de mi casa hay un parque.
3. En mi barrio no hay un acuario.   4. En el centro hay un cine.   5. En mi calle no hay muchos jóvenes.
6. En mi ciudad tenemos un polideportivo.   7. En mi barrio hay una calle peatonal.

UNIT 7.
Saying what I can do in my neighbourhood

¿Qué se puede hacer en tu barrio?	What can one do in your neighbourhood?
¿Adónde se puede ir?	Where can one go?
¿Qué se puede ver y visitar?	What can one see and visit?

En mi barrio se puede hacer muchas cosas	In my neighbourhood one can do many things

Por ejemplo, *For example,* **se puede** *one can* **me gusta** *I like to* **suelo** *I tend to*	**hacer** *to do*	**deporte** **equitación** **footing** **natación** **senderismo** **turismo**	*sport* *horse riding* *jogging* *swimming* *hiking* *sightseeing*	**en el bosque** *in the woods* **en el campo de fútbol** *on the football pitch* **en el casco antiguo** *in the old town* **en el centro comercial** *in the shopping mall* **en el centro de la ciudad** *in the city centre* **en el cine de mi barrio** *in my neighbourhood cinema* **en el club de tenis** *at the tennis club* **en el estadio** *in the stadium* **en el parque** *in the park* **en el polideportivo** *at the sports centre* **en la calle peatonal** *on the pedestrian street* **en la piscina** *in the swimming pool* **en la plaza mayor** *in the town square* **en la zona comercial de la ciudad** *in the commercial part of the city* **en la zona turística de la ciudad** *in the touristy part of the city*
	jugar *to play*	**al fútbol** **al golf** **al rugby**	*football* *golf* *rugby*	
	ir *to go*	**a conciertos** **al mercado** **de compras** **de marcha** **de paseo**	*to concerts* *to the market* *shopping* *clubbing* *for a walk*	
	ver *to see*	**películas** **un partido de fútbol**	*films* *a football game*	
	visitar *to visit*	**castillos** **galerías de arte** **mercados** **museos** **palacios históricos** **ruinas romanas**	*castles* *art galleries* *markets* *museums* *historic palaces* *Roman ruins*	

*Author's note: Watch out for expressions like **"hacer natación"** that are translated as *'to go'* swimming. The literal translation is actually *'to do'* swimming. The verbs **"hacer"** and **"ir"** often translate differently in Spanish and English, so watch out for them :)

THE LANGUAGE GYM

UNIT 7 – FIND SOMEONE WHO – Student Cards

Me gusta hacer turismo en el centro de la ciudad. **JUAN**	Me gusta ver películas en el cine de mi barrio. **ALBERTO**	Suelo visitar castillos en la zona turística de la ciudad. **SARA**	Me gusta visitar galerías de arte en el centro de la ciudad. **VALERIA**
Me gusta jugar al fútbol en el campo de fútbol. **RAQUEL**	Suelo ir de paseo en la calle peatonal. **JORGE**	Se puede ir de compras en la zona comercial de la ciudad. **CRISTINA**	Suelo jugar al rugby en el estadio. **PABLO**
Suelo hacer senderismo en el bosque. **JIMENA**	Se puede jugar al golf en el club de tenis. **LARA**	Me gusta ir a conciertos en la plaza mayor. **RAFAEL**	Se puede ir al mercado en la plaza mayor. **CHLOE**
Siempre voy de compras en la zona comercial de la ciudad. **MANUEL**	Me gusta hacer turismo en el centro de la ciudad. **GUILLERMO**	Se puede hacer footing en el parque. **NANCY**	Me gusta visitar galerías de arte en la plaza mayor. **TONI**

UNIT 7 – FIND SOMEONE WHO – Student Grid

¿Qué se puede hacer en tu barrio?	What can one do in your neighbourhood?
¿Adónde se puede ir?	Where can you go?
¿Qué se puede ver y visitar?	What can one see and visit?

	Find someone who...	Name(s)
1.	...can go to the market at the town square.	
2.	...regularly takes walks on the pedestrian street.	
3.	...likes to visit art galleries.	
4.	...likes to play football at the football field.	
5.	...often visits castles in the touristy part of the city.	
6.	...likes to watch movies at the neighbourhood cinema.	
7.	...plays rugby at the stadium.	
8.	...likes to go to concerts at the town square.	
9.	...likes to do sightseeing in the city centre.	
10.	...can go shopping in the commercial area of the city.	
11.	...can play golf at the tennis club.	
12.	...goes hiking in the forest.	
13.	...is a red herring! 🐟 (No match)	

UNIT 7 – ORAL PING-PONG – Person A

ENGLISH	SPANISH	ENGLISH	SPANISH
I like to do sightseeing in the city centre.	Me gusta hacer turismo en el centro de la ciudad.	One can do jogging in the park.	Se puede hacer footing en el parque.
One can swim in the pool at the sports centre.		I like to play football in the football field.	
I tend to take walks on the pedestrian street.	Suelo ir de paseo en la calle peatonal.	One can go to the market in the town square.	Se puede ir al mercado en la plaza mayor.
I like to visit art galleries in the shopping centre.		I tend to visit castles in the tourist area of the city.	
One can do sport at the tennis club.	Se puede hacer deporte en el club de tenis.	I like to swim in the pool at the sports centre.	Me gusta nadar en la piscina del polideportivo.
I like to watch movies in my neighbourhood cinema.		One can do hiking in the forest.	
One can visit museums in the old town.	Se puede visitar museos en el casco antiguo.	I like to go shopping in the commercial area of the city.	Me gusta ir de compras en la zona comercial de la ciudad.
I like to go to concerts in the town square.		One can play golf at the tennis club.	
I tend to play rugby at the stadium.	Suelo jugar al rugby en el estadio.	I tend to visit museums in the old town.	Suelo visitar museos en el casco antiguo.
I like to go clubbing in the touristy part of the city.		I like to watch films in my neighbourhood cinema.	

UNIT 7 – ORAL PING-PONG – Person B

ENGLISH	SPANISH	ENGLISH	SPANISH
I like to do sightseeing in the city centre.		One can do jogging in the park.	
One can swim in the pool at the sports centre.	Se puede nadar en la piscina del polideportivo.	I like to play football in the football field.	Me gusta jugar al fútbol en el campo de fútbol.
I tend to take walks on the pedestrian street.		One can go to the market in the town square.	
I like to visit art galleries in the shopping centre.	Me gusta visitar galerías de arte en el centro comercial.	I tend to visit castles in the tourist area of the city.	Suelo visitar castillos en la zona turística de la ciudad.
One can do sport at the tennis club.		I like to swim in the pool at the sports centre.	
I like to watch movies in my neighbourhood cinema.	Me gusta ver películas en el cine de mi barrio.	One can do hiking in the forest.	Se puede hacer senderismo en el bosque.
One can visit museums in the old town.		I like to go shopping in the commercial area of the city.	
I like to go to concerts in the town square.	Me gusta ir a conciertos en la plaza mayor.	One can play golf at the tennis club.	Se puede jugar al golf en el club de tenis.
I tend to play rugby at the stadium.		I tend to visit museums in the old town.	
I like to go clubbing in the touristy part of the city.	Me gusta ir de marcha en la zona turística de la ciudad.	I like to watch films in my neighbourhood cinema.	Me gusta ver películas en el cine de mi barrio.

 **THE LANGUAGE GYM**

No Snakes No Ladders

START						
1 I like to visit museums in the touristy part of the city.	**2** One can go to the market in the town square.	**3** I tend to play football on the football pitch.	**4** I like to go to my neighbourhood cinema.	**5** One can do hiking in the forest.	**6** What can one see and visit?	**7** Where can one go?
14 I like to do sightseeing in the city centre.	**13** One can do jogging in the park.	**12** What can one do in your neighbourhood?	**11** I like to watch movies in my neighbourhood cinema.	**10** One can do sport at the tennis club.	**9** I usually take a walk on the pedestrian street.	**8** I like to go shopping in the commercial part of the city.
17 I like to visit art galleries at the shopping mall.	**18** One can watch a football match at the stadium.	**19** I like to play rugby at the stadium.	**20** One can go clubbing in the touristy part of the city.	**21** What can one do in the shopping centre?	**22** I like to go to concerts in the town square.	**23** One can go for a walk in the park.
16 In my neighbourhood, one can do many things.	**29** One can visit museums in the city.	**28** I don't like to watch movies in my neighbourhood cinema.	**27** One can go shopping at the mall.	**26** I like to go to the market in the town square.	**25** One can visit historic palaces in the old town.	**24** What can one visit in your neighbourhood?
15 I tend to visit castles in the touristy part of the city.	**30** I like to play golf in the park.				FINISH	

THE LANGUAGE GYM

No Snakes No Ladders

7 ¿Adónde se puede ir?	**6** ¿Qué se puede ver y visitar?	**5** Se puede hacer senderismo en el bosque.	**4** Me gusta ir al cine de mi barrio.	**3** Suelo jugar al fútbol en el campo de fútbol.	**2** Se puede ir al mercado en la plaza mayor.
8 Me gusta ir de compras en la zona comercial de la ciudad.	**9** Suelo ir de paseo en la calle peatonal.	**10** Se puede hacer deporte en el club de tenis.	**11** Me gusta ver películas en el cine de mi barrio.	**12** ¿Qué se puede hacer en tu barrio?	**13** Se puede hacer footing en el parque.
23 Se puede ir de paseo en el parque.	**22** Me gusta ir a conciertos en la plaza mayor.	**21** ¿Qué se puede hacer en el centro comercial?	**20** Se puede ir de marcha en la zona turística de la ciudad.	**19** Me gusta jugar al rugby en el estadio.	**18** Se puede ver un partido de fútbol en el estadio.
24 ¿Qué se puede visitar en tu barrio?	**25** Se puede visitar palacios históricos en el casco antiguo.	**26** Me gusta ir al mercado en la plaza mayor.	**27** Se puede ir de compras en el centro comercial.	**28** No me gusta ver películas en el cine de mi barrio.	**29** Se puede visitar museos en la ciudad.

1 Me gusta visitar museos en la zona turística de la ciudad.	**14** Me gusta hacer turismo en el centro de la ciudad.	**17** Me gusta visitar galerías de arte en el centro comercial.	**30** Me gusta jugar al golf en el parque.
SALIDA	**15** Suelo visitar castillos en la zona turística de la ciudad.	**16** En mi barrio se puede hacer muchas cosas.	LLEGADA

THE LANGUAGE GYM

80

UNIT 7 – STAIRCASE TRANSLATION

In my neighbourhood, one can do lots of things.

In my neighbourhood, one can do lots of things. For example, one can do sightseeing.

In my neighbourhood, one can do lots of things. For example, one can do sightseeing in the old town.

In my neighbourhood, one can do lots of things. For example, one can do sightseeing in the old town. I like to go for a walk in the forest.

In my neighbourhood, one can do lots of things. For example, one can do sightseeing in the old town. I like to go for a walk in the forest. What can one do in your neighbourhood?

In my neighbourhood, one can do lots of things. For example, one can do sightseeing in the old town. I like to go for a walk in the forest. What can one do in your neighbourhood? I tend to go shopping in the commercial part of the city.

Translate the last step here:

⏱ UNIT 7 – FASTER! 🐇

Say:

	Time	Mistakes	Referee's name
1			
2			
3			
4			

1. I like to do sport at the sports centre.

2. One can go shopping in the commercial part of the city.

3. I tend to go for a walk on the pedestrian street.

4. I like to swim in the pool.

5. One can play football on the football pitch.

6. I like to watch movies in my neighbourhood cinema.

7. One can visit castles in the old town.

8. I like to play golf at the tennis club.

9. I tend to do jogging in the park.

10. One can go sightseeing in the city centre.

🕵 UNIT 7 – DETECTIVES & INFORMANTS 🕵‍♀

DETECTIVES	Spanish	English
¿Qué se puede hacer en tu barrio?		
¿A qué se puede jugar en tu ciudad?		
¿Qué se puede ver en tu barrio?		
¿Adónde se puede ir?		
¿Adónde sueles ir?		
¿Qué se puede visitar en tu ciudad?		
¿A qué te gusta jugar en tu barrio?		
¿Qué se puede hacer en el parque?		

INFORMANTS

En mi ciudad se puede jugar al fútbol en el estadio.	Se puede hacer senderismo en el parque.
En mi barrio me gusta jugar al rugby en el polideportivo.	En mi barrio se puede ver películas en el cine de mi barrio.
En mi barrio se puede hacer equitación en el bosque.	Se puede ir de marcha en la plaza mayor.
Suelo ir al mercado en el casco antiguo.	En mi ciudad se puede visitar palacios históricos en el centro de la ciudad.

UNIT 7 – COMMUNICATIVE DRILLS

1	2	3
What can one do in your neighbourhood? - In my neighbourhood, one can do sightseeing in the old town. **What can one visit?** - One can visit castles and museums.	**Where can one go?** - One can go to the shopping centre. **What can one do?** - One can go shopping and visit art galleries.	**What do you tend to do in your city?** - In my city, I tend to watch films in my neighbourhood cinema. And you? **In my neighbourhood, I tend to visit the Roman ruins.**

4	5	6
What can one play in your neighbourhood? - One can play golf, but I tend to play football in the park. **What can one visit?** - I like to visit the museums in the town square.	**What can you do in your city?** - You can do lots of things. For example, you can do jogging in the pedestrian street. **Where can you go?** - I tend to go clubbing in city centre.	**What do you like to do in your city?** - I like to watch a football match in the stadium. And you? **I tend to go to concerts in the stadium.**

7	8	9
Where can one go in your neighbourhood? - In my neighbourhood, one can go for a walk in the shopping mall. **What can one do?** - One can do swimming in the swimming pool.	**I like to do horse riding. What can one do in your town?** - I tend to play football on the football pitch. I like football and rugby. **I tend to play rugby at the park.**	**What can one do in your neighbourhood?** - In my neighbourhood, one can do many things. **What can one watch?** - One can watch a football match at the park.

UNIT 7 – COMMUNICATIVE DRILLS
REFEREE CARD

1	2	3
¿Qué se puede hacer en tu barrio? - En mi barrio se puede hacer turismo en el casco antiguo. **¿Qué se puede visitar?** - Se puede visitar castillos y museos.	**¿Dónde se puede ir?** - Se puede ir al centro comercial. **¿Qué se puede hacer?** - Se puede ir de compras y visitar galerías de arte.	**¿Qué sueles hacer en tu ciudad?** - En mi ciudad suelo ver películas en el cine de mi barrio. ¿Y tú? **En mi barrio suelo visitar las ruinas romanas.**

4	5	6
¿A qué se puede jugar en tu barrio? Se puede jugar al golf, pero suelo jugar al fútbol en el parque. **¿Qué se puede visitar?** Me gusta visitar los museos en la plaza mayor.	**¿Qué se puede hacer en tu ciudad?** - Se puede hacer muchas cosas. Por ejemplo, se puede hacer footing en la calle peatonal. **¿Adónde se puede ir?** - Suelo ir de marcha en el centro de la ciudad.	**¿Qué te gusta hacer en tu ciudad?** - Me gusta ver un partido de fútbol en el estadio. ¿Y tú? **Suelo ir a conciertos en el estadio.**

7	8	9
¿Adónde se puede ir en tu barrio? - En mi barrio se puede ir de paseo en el centro comercial. **¿Qué se puede hacer?** - Se puede hacer natación en la piscina.	**Me gusta hacer equitación. ¿Qué se puede hacer en tu ciudad?** - Suelo jugar al fútbol en el campo de fútbol. Me gusta el fútbol y el rugby. **Suelo jugar al rugby en el parque.**	**¿Qué se puede hacer en tu barrio?** - En mi barrio se puede hacer muchas cosas. **¿Qué se puede ver?** - Se puede ver un partido de fútbol en el parque.

UNIT 7 – SURVEY

	¿Cómo te llamas? *What is your name?*	¿Qué se puede hacer en el parque? *What can one do in the park?*	¿Adónde sueles ir? *Where does one tend to go?*	¿Qué se puede hacer en tu barrio? *What can one do in your neighbourhood?*	¿Qué se puede ver en tu barrio? *What can one see in your neighbourhood?*	¿Qué se puede visitar en tu ciudad? *What can one visit in your city?*
e.g.	Me llamo Juan.	Se puede hacer footing en el parque.	Suelo ir de compras en el centro comercial.	En mi barrio se puede hacer turismo en el casco antiguo.	Se puede ver películas en el cine.	Se puede visitar galerías de arte en la plaza mayor.
1.						
2.						
3.						
4.						
5.						
6.						
7.						

UNIT 7 – ANSWERS

FIND SOMEONE WHO

Find someone who...	Name(s)
1. ...can go to the market at the town square.	**Chloe**
2. ...regularly takes walks on the pedestrian street.	**Jorge**
3. ...likes to visit art galleries.	**Valeria/Toni**
4. ...likes to play football at the football field.	**Raquel**
5. ...often visits castles in the touristy part of the city.	**Sara**
6. ...likes to watch movies at the neighbourhood cinema.	**Alberto**
7. ...plays rugby at the stadium.	**Pablo**
8. ...likes to go to concerts at the town square.	**Rafael**
9. ...likes to do sightseeing in the city centre.	**Juan/Guillermo**
10. ...can go shopping in the commercial area of the city.	**Manuel/Cristina**
11. ...can play golf at the tennis club.	**Lara**
12. ...goes hiking in the forest.	**Jimena**
13. ...is a red herring! 🐟 (No match)	**Nancy**

STAIRCASE TRANSLATION

En mi barrio se puede hacer muchas cosas. Por ejemplo, se puede hacer turismo en el casco antiguo. Me gusta ir de paseo en el bosque. ¿Qué se puede hacer en tu barrio? Suelo ir de compras en la zona comercial de la ciudad.

FASTER!

REFEREE SOLUTION:
1. Me gusta hacer deporte en el polideportivo.   2. Se puede ir de compras en la parte comercial de la ciudad.
3. Suelo dar paseos por la calle peatonal.   4. Me gusta nadar en la piscina.
5. Se puede jugar al fútbol en el campo de fútbol.   6. Me gusta ver películas en el cine de mi barrio.
7. Se puede visitar castillos en el casco antiguo.   8. Me gusta jugar al golf en el club de tenis.
9. Suelo hacer footing en el parque.   10. Se puede hacer turismo en el centro de la ciudad.

DETECTIVES & INFORMANTS

DETECTIVES	Spanish	English
¿Qué se puede hacer en tu barrio?	Se puede hacer equitación en el bosque.	One can do horse riding in the forest.
¿A qué se puede jugar en tu ciudad?	Se puede jugar al fútbol en el estadio.	One can play football at the stadium.
¿Qué se puede ver en tu barrio?	Se puede ver películas en el cine de mi barrio.	One can watch films in my neighbourhood cinema.
¿Adónde se puede ir?	Se puede ir de marcha en la plaza mayor.	One can go out in the town square.
¿Adónde sueles ir?	Suelo ir al mercado en el casco antiguo.	I tend to go to the market in the old town.
¿Qué se pude visitar en tu ciudad?	Se puede visitar palacios históricos en el centro de la ciudad.	One can visit historic palaces in the city centre.
¿A qué te gusta jugar en tu barrio?	Me gusta jugar al rugby en el polideportivo.	I like to play rugby at the sports centre.
¿Qué se puede hacer en el parque?	Se puede hacer senderismo en el parque.	One can go hiking in the park.

UNIT 8.
Describing my street

INSTRUCTIONS FOR ALL GAMES ARE ON PAGES 1-2

¿Qué hay en tu calle?	What is there on your street?
¿Dónde está tu casa?	Where is your house?
¿Qué sitios hay en tu barrio?	What places are there in your neighbourhood?

	Masculine nouns		Feminine nouns	
En mi calle hay *On my street there is* **Cerca de mi casa hay** *Near my house there is*	un aparcamiento	*a car park*	una biblioteca	*a library*
	un campo de fútbol	*a football pitch*	una carnicería	*a butcher's*
	un centro comercial	*a shopping mall*	una estación de tren	*a train station*
	un edificio	*a building*	una iglesia	*a church*
	un polideportivo	*a sports centre*	una mezquita	*a mosque*
	un parque pequeño	*a small park*	una panadería	*a bakery*
	un restaurante chino	*a chinese restaurant*	una piscina municipal	*a local pool*
	un supermercado	*a supermarket*	una sinagoga	*a synagogue*
	un teatro	*a theatre*	una zapatería	*a shoe shop*
	una tienda de	*a ... shop*	deporte	*sport*
			música	*music*
			ropa	*clothes*

			Feminine nouns	
El cine *The cinema* **Mi casa** *My house* **Mi edificio** *My building* **Mi piso** *My flat*	**está** *is*	a la derecha	*to the right*	
		a la izquierda	*to the left*	
		al lado	*next to*	**de la** *of/from*
		cerca	*near*	biblioteca
		delante	*in front*	carnicería
		detrás	*behind*	panadería
		enfrente	*opposite*	piscina
		en la esquina	*on the corner*	tienda de música
		lejos	*far*	**Masc. nouns**
		a diez minutos a pie *a 10 minute walk away*		**del** *of/from*
				campo de fútbol
		a diez minutos en coche *a 10 minute car ride away*		centro comercial
				colegio
				estadio
				museo
				parque
		al final de la calle	*at the end of the street*	

Mi casa Mi piso	**está**	**entre** *between*	la carnicería el cine	**y**	el supermercado la piscina

No hay *There is not*	**ningún** *any (m – sg.)*	polideportivo *sports centre*	cerca de donde vivo	*near where I live*
	ninguna *any (f – sg.)*	tienda buena *good shop*	en mi barrio por aquí	*in my neighbourhood* *around here*

UNIT 8 – FIND SOMEONE WHO – Student Cards

En mi calle hay una panadería y mi casa está al lado de una sinagoga. **JUANA**	Cerca de mi casa hay una estación de tren. **FEDERICO**	En mi calle hay un campo de fútbol. **ÚRSULA**	Cerca de mi casa hay una biblioteca. **MACY**
Cerca de mi casa hay una piscina municipal. **TOBY**	Mi casa está al lado de una sinagoga. **DANIELA**	Mi edificio está enfrente del colegio. **REBECCA**	Mi casa está a diez minutos a pie del parque. **ALEJANDRO**
En mi calle hay una estación de tren. **QUINO**	Mi piso está al final de la calle. **FILIPPO**	Mi piso está detrás del centro comercial. **CLAUDIA**	Mi piso está entre la piscina y el cine. **LUCAS**
Mi casa está al lado del campo de fútbol. **JORGE**	Mi casa está entre la carnicería y el supermercado. **SIMON**	Mi casa está cerca de la biblioteca. **RYAN**	Mi piso está delante del estadio. **MARÍA**

UNIT 8 – FIND SOMEONE WHO – Student Grid

¿Qué hay en tu calle? ¿Dónde está tu casa? ¿Qué sitios hay en tu barrio?	*What is there on your street?* *Where is your house?* *What places are there in your neighbourhood?*	
Find someone who...		**Name(s)**
1.	...lives in a flat at the end of the street.	
2.	...lives in a house next to a football field.	
3.	...lives in a house between a butcher's and a supermarket.	
4.	...lives near a train station.	
5.	...lives near a local swimming pool.	
6.	...has a football pitch on their street.	
7.	...lives next to a synagogue.	
8.	...lives opposite a school.	
9.	...lives a ten-minute walk away from a park.	
10.	...lives in a flat behind the shopping centre.	
11.	...lives in a flat between the swimming pool and the cinema.	
12.	...lives in a house near the library.	
13.	...is a red herring! 🐟 (No match)	

 THE LANGUAGE GYM

ENGLISH	SPANISH	ENGLISH	SPANISH
The cinema is next to the music shop.	El cine está al lado de la tienda de música.	There isn't a sports centre around here.	No hay ningún polideportivo por aquí.
My building is opposite the stadium.		My house is between the butcher's and the cinema.	
My flat is to the left of the shopping centre.	Mi piso está a la izquierda del centro comercial.	The cinema is behind my building.	El cine está detrás de mi edificio.
My house is on the corner of the football pitch.		My building is in front of the library.	
On my street, there is a small park.	En mi calle hay un parque pequeño.	My flat is a ten-minute walk away from the park.	Mi piso está a diez minutos a pie del parque.
Near my house, there is a bakery.		On my street, there is a supermarket.	
Near my house, there is a football pitch.	Cerca de mi casa hay un campo de fútbol.	Near my house, there is a train station.	Cerca de mi casa hay una estación de tren.
There isn't a sports centre near where I live.		On my street, there is a shoe shop.	
On my street, there is a church and a bakery.	En mi calle hay una iglesia y una panadería.	There isn't a good shop in my neighbourhood.	No hay ninguna tienda buena en mi barrio.
Near my house, there is a local pool.		My flat is between the cinema and the supermarket.	

ENGLISH	SPANISH	ENGLISH	SPANISH
The cinema is next to the music shop.		There isn't a sports centre around here.	
My building is opposite the stadium.	Mi edificio está enfrente del estadio.	My house is between the butcher's and the cinema.	Mi casa está entre la carnicería y el cine.
My flat is to the left of the shopping centre.		The cinema is behind my building.	
My house is on the corner of the football pitch.	Mi casa está en la esquina del campo de fútbol.	My building is in front of the library.	Mi edificio está delante de la biblioteca.
On my street, there is a small park.		My flat is a ten-minute walk away from the park.	
Near my house, there is a bakery.	Cerca de mi casa hay una panadería.	On my street, there is a supermarket.	En mi calle hay un supermercado.
Near my house, there is a football pitch.		Near my house, there is a train station.	
There isn't a sports centre near where I live.	No hay ningún polideportivo cerca de donde vivo.	On my street, there is a shoe shop.	En mi calle hay una zapatería.
On my street, there is a church and a bakery.		There isn't a good shop in my neighbourhood.	
Near my house, there is a local pool.	Cerca de mi casa hay una piscina municipal.	My flat is between the cinema and the supermarket.	Mi piso está entre el cine y el supermercado.

THE LANGUAGE GYM

No Snakes No Ladders

START

1 On my street, there is a bakery.

2 On my street, there is a church.

3 My house is close to the bakery.

4 My house is between the butcher's and the cinema.

5 My building is at the end of the street.

6 My flat is near the bakery.

7 What places are there in your neighbourhood?

8 The cinema is to the right of my building.

9 There isn't a sports centre near where I live.

10 Near my house, there is a train station.

11 On my street, there is a shopping centre.

12 There aren't any good shops in my neighbourhood.

13 My house is opposite the library.

14 My flat is between the cinema and the supermarket.

15 On my street, there is a mosque.

16 Where is your house?

17 There isn't a football pitch around here.

18 My building is behind the museum.

19 My flat is next to the shopping centre.

20 My house is near the football pitch.

21 My house is opposite the stadium.

22 Near my house, there is a supermarket.

23 On my street, there is a butcher's.

24 Near my house, there is a small park.

25 On my street, there is a church.

26 Near my house, there is a local pool.

27 There isn't a good shop near my house.

28 What is there on your street?

29 My house is at the end of the street.

30 My house is a ten-minute walk away from the park.

FINISH

No Snakes No Ladders

SALIDA

1 En mi calle hay una panadería.	**2** En mi calle hay una iglesia.	**3** Mi casa está cerca de la panadería.	**4** Mi casa está entre la carnicería y el cine.	**5** Mi edificio está al final de la calle.	**6** Mi piso está cerca de la panadería.	**7** ¿Qué sitios hay en tu barrio?
14 Mi piso está entre el cine y el supermercado.	**13** Mi casa está enfrente de la biblioteca.	**12** No hay ninguna tienda buena en mi barrio.	**11** En mi calle hay un centro comercial.	**10** Cerca de mi casa hay una estación de tren.	**9** No hay ningún polideportivo cerca de donde vivo.	**8** El cine está a la derecha de mi edificio.
15 En mi calle hay una mezquita.	**16** ¿Dónde está tu casa?	**19** Mi piso está al lado del centro comercial.	**20** Mi casa está cerca del campo de fútbol.	**21** Mi casa está enfrente del estadio.	**22** Cerca de mi casa hay un supermercado.	**23** En mi calle hay una carnicería.
17 No hay ningún campo de fútbol por aquí.	**18** Mi edificio está detrás del museo.	**28** ¿Qué hay en tu calle?	**27** No hay ninguna tienda buena cerca de mi casa.	**26** Cerca de mi casa hay una piscina municipal.	**25** En mi calle hay una iglesia.	**24** Cerca de mi casa hay un parque pequeño.
30 Mi casa está a diez minutos a pie del parque.	**29** Mi casa está al final de la calle.					

LLEGADA

THE LANGUAGE GYM

UNIT 8 – STAIRCASE TRANSLATION

On my street, there is a supermarket and a church.

On my street, there is a supermarket and a church. Near my house, there is a train station.

On my street, there is a supermarket and a church. Near my house, there is a train station. Where is your house?

On my street, there is a supermarket and a church. Near my house, there is a train station. Where is your house? My house is between the cinema and the swimming pool.

On my street, there is a supermarket and a church. Near my house, there is a train station. Where is your house? My house is between the cinema and the swimming pool. There isn't a good shop in my neighbourhood.

On my street, there is a supermarket and a church. Near my house, there is a train station. Where is your house? My house is between the cinema and the swimming pool. There isn't a good shop in my neighbourhood. What places are there in your neighbourhood?

Translate the last step here:

⏱ UNIT 8 – FASTER! 🖋

Say:

1. Near my house, there is a bakery.
2. On my street, there is a music shop.
3. The cinema is next to the library.
4. What is there on your street?
5. My flat is a ten-minute walk away from the school.
6. My building is behind the football pitch.
7. There isn't a sports centre around here.
8. My house is between the butcher's and the stadium.
9. My flat is between the cinema and the swimming pool.
10. What places are there in your neighbourhood?

	Time	Mistakes	Referee's name
1			
2			
3			
4			

UNIT 8 – FAST & FURIOUS
Focus on prepositions of place

1. Mi casa está _____ _____ del colegio.   *next to*

2. Mi piso está _____ del centro comercial.   *in front*

3. El museo está ____ ____ _____ del campo de fútbol. *on the corner of*

4. La biblioteca está _____ de la carnicería.   *behind*

5. El cine está _____ del parque.   *far*

6. Mi casa está ___ ____ _____ de la panadería. *to the right*

7. Mi edificio está _____ del museo.   *opposite*

8. El restaurante italiano está _____ de la zapatería. *close*

9. El aparcamiento está ___ _____ _____ de la mezquita. *to the left*

10. La estación de tren está ____ _____ ____ ____ _____. *at the end of the street*

	Time 1	Time 2	Time 3	Time 4
Time				
Mistakes				

THE LANGUAGE GYM

94

UNIT 8 – COMMUNICATIVE DRILLS

1	2	3
Where is your house? - My house is near the music shop. **What is there on your street?** - On my street, there is a supermarket and a shoe shop.	**What places are there in your neighbourhood?** - In my neighbourhood, there is a shopping mall, a small park and a bakery. And you? What is in your neighbourhood? **Near my house, there is a church and a mosque.**	**My house is between the cinema and the sports centre. Where is your house?** - My house is a ten-minute walk away from the theatre. It is opposite the library.

4	5	6
What is there on your street? - On my street, there is a sports shop and a train station. **Where is the cinema?** - The cinema is next to the school.	**Is there a shop near your house?** - There isn't a good shop near my house. However, there is a sports centre on my street.	**Where is your flat?** - My flat is a ten-minute car ride away from the park. **What is there on your street?** - On my street, there is a football pitch and a Chinese restaurant.

7	8	9
Where is your building? - My building is to the left of the museum and opposite the stadium. **Is there a sports centre?** - No, there is not a sports centre in my neighbourhood.	**On my street, there is a small park and a football pitch. What is there on your street?** - On my street, there is a supermarket and a shoe shop. My house is in between the school and the synagogue.	**What places are there in your neighbourhood?** - In my neighbourhood, there is an Italian restaurant. It is behind the shopping mall. **There isn't an Italian restaurant near where I live.**

1	2	3
¿Dónde está tu casa? - Mi casa está cerca de la tienda de música. **¿Qué hay en tu calle?** - En mi calle hay un supermercado y una zapatería.	**¿Qué sitios hay en tu barrio?** - En mi barrio hay un centro comercial, un parque pequeño y una panadería. ¿Y tú? ¿Qué hay en tu barrio? **Cerca de mi casa hay una iglesia y una mezquita.**	**Mi casa está entre el cine y el polideportivo. ¿Dónde está tu casa?** - Mi casa está a diez minutos a pie del teatro. Está enfrente de la biblioteca.

4	5	6
¿Qué hay en tu calle? - En mi calle hay una tienda de deportes y una estación de tren. **¿Dónde está el cine?** - El cine está al lado del colegio.	**¿Hay alguna tienda cerca de tu casa?** - No hay ninguna tienda buena cerca de mi casa. Sin embargo, hay un polideportivo en mi calle.	**¿Dónde está tu piso?** - Mi piso está a diez minutos en coche del parque. **¿Qué hay en tu calle?** - En mi calle hay un campo de fútbol y un restaurante chino.

7	8	9
¿Dónde está tu edificio? - Mi edificio está a la izquierda del museo y enfrente del estadio. **¿Hay un polideportivo?** - No, no hay ningún polideportivo en mi barrio.	**En mi calle hay un parque pequeño y un campo de fútbol. ¿Qué hay en tu calle?** - En mi calle hay un supermercado y una zapatería. Mi casa está entre el colegio y la sinagoga.	**¿Qué sitios hay en tu barrio?** - En mi barrio hay un restaurante italiano. Está detrás del centro comercial. **No hay ningún restaurante italiano cerca de donde vivo.**

UNIT 8 – SURVEY

	¿Cómo te llamas? *What is your name?*	¿Qué hay en tu calle? *What is there on your street?*	¿Dónde está tu casa? *Where is your house?*	¿Qué sitios hay en tu barrio? *What places are there in your neighbourhood?*	¿Dónde está el cine? *Where is the cinema?*	¿Hay un polideportivo cerca de dónde vives? *Is there a sports centre near where you live?*
e.g.	Me llamo Juan.	En mi calle hay un supermercado.	Mi casa está cerca del parque.	En mi barrio hay una iglesia y un teatro.	El cine está entre la biblioteca y la carnicería.	No hay ningún polideportivo por aquí.
1.						
2.						
3.						
4.						
5.						
6.						
7.						

UNIT 8 – ANSWERS

FIND SOMEONE WHO

	Find someone who/whose...	Name(s)
1.	...lives in a flat at the end of the street.	**Filippo**
2.	...lives in a house next to a football field.	**Jorge**
3.	...lives in a house between a butcher's and a supermarket.	**Simon**
4.	...lives near a train station.	**Federico/Quino**
5.	...lives near a local swimming pool.	**Toby**
6.	...has a football pitch on their street.	**Úrsula**
7.	...lives next to a synagogue.	**Juana/Daniela**
8.	...lives in front of a school.	**Rebecca**
9.	...lives a ten-minute walk away from a park.	**Alejandro**
10.	...lives in a flat behind the shopping centre.	**Claudia**
11.	...lives in a flat between the swimming pool and the cinema.	**Lucas**
12.	...lives in a house near the library.	**Ryan/Macy**
13.	...is a red herring! 🐟 (No match)	**María**

STAIRCASE TRANSLATION

En mi calle hay un supermercado y una iglesia. Cerca de mi casa hay una estación de tren. ¿Dónde está tu casa? Mi casa está entre el cine y la piscina. No hay ninguna tienda buena en mi barrio. ¿Qué sitios hay en tu barrio?

FASTER!

REFEREE SOLUTION:
1. Cerca de mi casa hay una panadería.   2. En mi calle hay una tienda de música.
3. El cine está al lado de la biblioteca.   4. ¿Qué hay en tu calle?   5. Mi piso está a diez minutos a pie del colegio.
6. Mi edificio está detrás del campo de fútbol.   7. No hay ningún polideportivo por aquí.
8. Mi casa está entre la carnicería y el estadio.   9. Mi piso está entre el cine y la piscina.
10. ¿Qué sitios hay en tu barrio?

FAST & FURIOUS

1. Mi casa está **al lado** del colegio.   2. Mi piso está **delante** del centro comercial.
3. El museo está **en la esquina** del campo de fútbol.   4. La biblioteca está **detrás** de la carnicería.
5. El cine está **lejos** del parque.   6. Mi casa está **a la derecha** de la panadería.
7. Mi edificio está **enfrente** del museo.   8. El restaurante italiano está **cerca** de la zapatería.
9. El aparcamiento está **a la izquierda** de la mezquita.   10. La estación de tren está **al final de la calle**.

UNIT 9. Describing my home & furniture

¿Cuántas habitaciones hay en tu casa?	How many rooms are there in your house?
¿Te gusta tu casa? ¿Por qué?	Do you like your house? Why?
¿Qué hay en la cocina / el salón?	What is there in the kitchen / living room?

Vivo en	una casa	a house	en	el campo	the countryside
	un piso	a flat	in	el centro de la ciudad	the city centre
				la costa	the coast
	un edificio	a building		la montaña	the mountains
				las afueras	the outskirts

En mi casa *In my house*	hay *there are*	cinco seis siete	habitaciones, *rooms,*	por ejemplo, *for example*	el dormitorio de mis padres *my parents' bedroom*	
					mi dormitorio	my bedroom
				como *such as*	una cocina	a kitchen
En mi piso *In my flat*					una sala de juegos	a playroom
					un comedor	a dining room
					un cuarto de baño	a bathroom
					un salón	a living room

también hay *there is also*	un desván	an attic	y	un garaje	a garage
	un sótano	a basement		un jardín	a garden

Me gusta mi casa porque *I like my house because*	*es *it is*	acogedora	cosy	espaciosa	spacious
		antigua	old	grande	big
		bonita	beautiful	luminosa	well lit
		fea	ugly	pequeña	small
No me gusta mi casa porque *I don't like my house because*	está *it is*	bien amueblada	well furnished		
		limpia	clean		
		sucia	dirty		

Me gusta mi piso porque *I like my flat because*	es	acogedor		espacioso	
		antiguo		grande	
		bonito		luminoso	
		feo		pequeño	
No me gusta mi piso porque *I don't like my flat because*	está	bien amueblado			
		limpio			
		sucio			

En la cocina hay		En el salón hay		En mi dormitorio hay	
un horno	an oven	un sillón	an armchair	un armario	a wardrobe
un lavaplatos	a dishwasher	un sofá		un escritorio	a desk
				un espejo	a mirror
una despensa	a pantry	una alfombra	a rug	un ordenador	a computer
una mesa	a table	una mesa	a table		
una nevera	a fridge	una mesita	a coffee table	una cama	a bed
una silla	a chair	una televisión		una estantería	a bookshelf
				cortinas	curtains

*Author's note: As mentioned earlier in the book, **"es"** (*it is*) and **"está"** (*it is*) are used for different purposes. You will see them used in context throughout this unit. For a full explanation or **ser & estar** and accompanying activities, please see the relevant sections in our Spanish Verb Pivots book ☺

UNIT 9 – FIND SOMEONE WHO – Student Cards

Vivo en una casa en las afueras. **ANA**	Me gusta mi casa porque es acogedora. **RAÚL**	Vivo en un edificio en la costa. **ISABEL**	En mi casa hay seis habitaciones. Por ejemplo, hay un comedor. **FERNANDO**
Vivo en una casa en el centro de la ciudad. **XAVIER**	En mi casa hay siete habitaciones. Por ejemplo, hay un cuarto de baño. **LOUIS**	En mi casa hay seis habitaciones. Por ejemplo, hay un comedor. **BELÉN**	No me gusta mi casa porque es fea. **SONIA**
En mi casa hay cinco habitaciones, como el dormitorio de mis padres. **FABIO**	En mi piso hay cinco habitaciones. Por ejemplo, hay una sala de juegos. **PAULA**	Vivo en una casa en las afueras. **LOURDES**	Vivo en un piso en el centro de la ciudad. **RAFA**
Mi casa está en el centro de la ciudad. **ALBERTO**	No me gusta mi casa porque no está bien amueblada. **PATRICIA**	No me gusta mi casa porque es antigua. **ROSA**	En mi casa hay cinco habitaciones, como un salón. **ADA**

UNIT 9 – FIND SOMEONE WHO – Student Grid

¿Cuántas habitaciones hay en tu casa? ¿Te gusta tu casa? ¿Dónde está tu casa?	*What is there in your house?* *Do you like your house?* *Where is your house?*	
Find someone who...		**Name(s)**
1.	...mentions their bathroom.	
2.	...has six rooms in their house, one being a dining room.	
3.	...mentions a living room.	
4.	...dislikes their house because it is old.	
5.	...lives in a building on the coast.	
6.	...dislikes their house because it is not well furnished.	
7.	...likes their house because it is cosy.	
8.	...dislikes their house because it is ugly.	
9.	...lives in a house on the outskirts.	
10.	...lives in the city centre.	
11.	...mentions their parents bedroom.	
12.	...is a red herring! 🐟 (No match)	

UNIT 9 – ORAL PING-PONG – Person A

ENGLISH	SPANISH	ENGLISH	SPANISH
In the kitchen, there is an oven and a table.	En la cocina hay un horno y una mesa.	What is there in the living room?	¿Qué hay en el salón?
In the kitchen, there is a fridge, a dishwasher, and a table.		I like my house because it's big.	
In my bedroom, there is a bed, a wardrobe, and curtains.	En mi dormitorio hay una cama, un armario y cortinas.	In the living room, there is a sofa and a television.	En el salón hay un sofá y una televisión.
I don't like my house because it is dirty.		How many rooms are there in your house?	
In my house, there are five rooms, such as my parents' bedroom.	En mi casa hay cinco habitaciones, como el dormitorio de mis padres.	In my flat, there are seven rooms, such as a kitchen.	En mi piso hay siete habitaciones, como una cocina.
I live in a house in the mountains.		In the kitchen, there is an oven and a fridge.	
I live in a house on the outskirts.	Vivo en una casa en las afueras.	In my bedroom, there is a mirror and a bed.	En mi dormitorio hay un espejo y una cama.
How many rooms are there in your house?		Do you like your house?	
In my bedroom, there is a desk and a mirror.	En mi dormitorio hay un escritorio y un espejo.	I like my flat because it's spacious.	Me gusta mi piso porque es espacioso.
In the living room, there is a rug and a sofa.		I don't like my flat because it's small.	

UNIT 9 – ORAL PING-PONG – Person B

ENGLISH	SPANISH	ENGLISH	SPANISH
In the kitchen, there is an oven and a table.		What is there in the living room?	
In the kitchen, there is a fridge, a dishwasher, and a table.	En la cocina hay una nevera, un lavaplatos y una mesa.	I like my house because it's big.	Me gusta mi casa porque es grande.
In my bedroom, there is a bed, a wardrobe, and curtains.		In the living room, there is a sofa and a television.	
I don't like my house because it is dirty.	No me gusta mi casa porque está sucia.	How many rooms are there in your house?	¿Cuántas habitaciones hay en tu casa?
In my house, there are five rooms, such as my parents' bedroom.		In my flat, there are seven rooms, such as a kitchen.	
I live in a house in the mountains.	Vivo en una casa en la montaña.	In the kitchen, there is an oven and a fridge.	En la cocina hay un horno y una nevera.
I live in a house on the outskirts.		In my bedroom, there is a mirror and a bed.	
How many rooms are there in your house?	¿Cuántas habitaciones hay en tu casa?	Do you like your house?	¿Te gusta tu casa?
In my bedroom, there is a desk and a mirror.		I like my flat because it's spacious.	
In the living room, there is a rug and a sofa.	En el salón hay una alfombra y un sofá.	I don't like my flat because it's small.	No me gusta mi piso porque es pequeño.

THE LANGUAGE GYM

No Snakes No Ladders

7 I live in a house on the coast.	**8** How many rooms are there in your house?	**23** In my bedroom, there is a desk, a mirror, and a computer.	**24** I like my flat because it's well furnished.				
6 In my flat, there are six rooms, such as my bedroom.	**9** I live in a house in the city centre.	**22** Do you like your flat?	**25** I don't like my flat because it's dirty.				
5 In my flat, there are six rooms. For example, there is a dining room.	**10** I like my flat because it is well lit.	**21** In my house, there are seven rooms, such as a kitchen.	**26** I live in a house in the countryside.				
4 I don't like my house because it is small.	**11** In my bedroom, there is a wardrobe, a bed, and curtains.	**20** In the kitchen, there is a pantry, a table, and a chair.	**27** Do you like your house?				
3 I like my flat because it is clean.	**12** In my flat, there are seven rooms, such as a bathroom.	**19** In my flat, there are five rooms. For example, there is my bedroom.	**28** In the kitchen, there is a fridge and a chair.				
2 In the living room, there is a coffee table and an armchair.	**13** I live in a building in the mountains.	**18** In my flat, there are five rooms, such as a living room.	**29** I don't like my flat because it's ugly.				
1 In my bedroom, there is a wardrobe and curtains.	**14** What is there in the kitchen?	**17** I like my house because it's well furnished.	**30** I like my house because it's beautiful.				
START	**15** I live in a flat on the outskirts.	**16** I live in a flat in the mountains.	**FINISH**				

THE LANGUAGE GYM

103

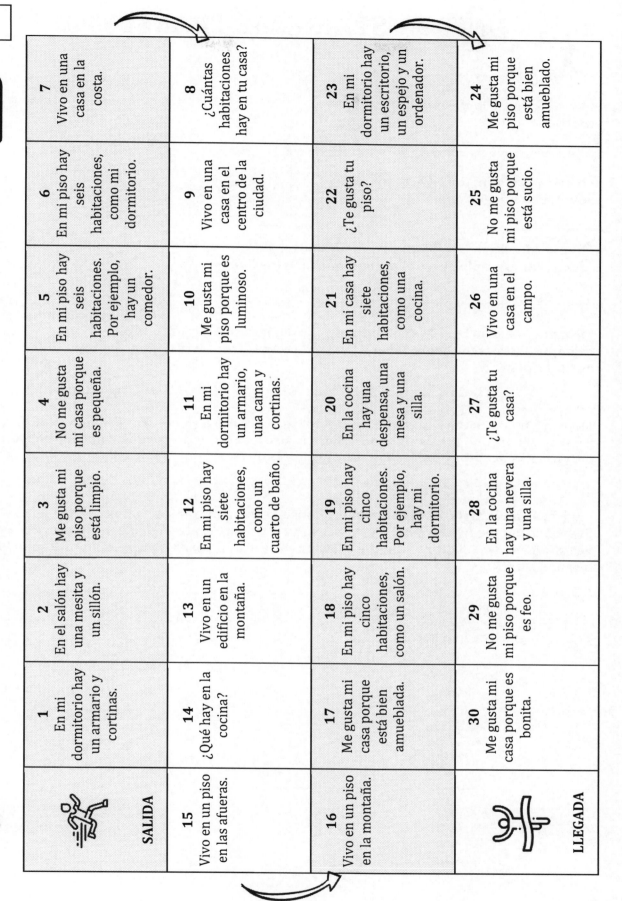

UNIT 9

No Snakes No Ladders

SALIDA

1 En mi dormitorio hay un armario y cortinas.	**2** En el salón hay una mesita y un sillón.	**3** Me gusta mi piso porque está limpio.	**4** No me gusta mi casa porque es pequeña.	**5** En mi piso hay seis habitaciones. Por ejemplo, hay un comedor.	**6** En mi piso hay seis habitaciones, como mi dormitorio.	**7** Vivo en una casa en la costa.	
14 ¿Qué hay en la cocina?	**13** Vivo en un edificio en la montaña.	**12** En mi piso hay siete habitaciones, como un cuarto de baño.	**11** En mi dormitorio hay un armario, una cama y cortinas.	**10** Me gusta mi piso porque es luminoso.	**9** Vivo en una casa en el centro de la ciudad.	**8** ¿Cuántas habitaciones hay en tu casa?	
15 Vivo en un piso en las afueras.							
16 Vivo en un piso en la montaña.	**17** Me gusta mi casa porque está bien amueblada.	**18** En mi piso hay cinco habitaciones, como un salón.	**19** En mi piso hay cinco habitaciones. Por ejemplo, hay mi dormitorio.	**20** En la cocina hay una despensa, una mesa y una silla.	**21** En mi casa hay siete habitaciones, como una cocina.	**22** ¿Te gusta tu piso?	**23** En mi dormitorio hay un escritorio, un espejo y un ordenador.
30 Me gusta mi casa porque es bonita.	**29** No me gusta mi piso porque es feo.	**28** En la cocina hay una nevera y una silla.	**27** ¿Te gusta tu casa?	**26** Vivo en una casa en el campo.	**25** No me gusta mi piso porque está sucio.	**24** Me gusta mi piso porque está bien amueblado.	

LLEGADA

THE LANGUAGE GYM

104

UNIT 9 – STAIRCASE TRANSLATION

I live in a house in the city centre.

I live in a house in the city centre. In my house, there are 6 rooms.

I live in a house in the city centre. In my house, there are 6 rooms. For example, there is my bedroom and the living room.

I live in a house in the city centre. In my house, there are 6 rooms. For example, there is my bedroom and the living room. There is also an attic and a garden.

I live in a house in the city centre. In my house, there are 6 rooms. For example, there is my bedroom and the living room. There is also an attic and a garden. I like my house because it is beautiful and well lit. However, it is dirty.

I live in a house in the city centre. In my house, there are 6 rooms. For example, there is my bedroom and the living room. There is also an attic and a garden. I like my house because it is beautiful and well lit. However, it is dirty. In the kitchen, there is an oven. In my room, there is a bed and a desk.

Translate the last step here:

🕙 UNIT 9 – FASTER! 💨

Say:

1. En el salón hay una televisión y un sofá.

2. ¿Te gusta tu casa?

3. Vivo en un piso en la costa.

4. En mi casa hay cinco habitaciones, como una sala de juegos.

5. Me gusta mi casa porque es luminosa.

6. Vivo en un edificio en las afueras.

7. En mi casa hay seis habitaciones, como mi dormitorio.

8. En la cocina hay un lavaplatos y una silla.

9. En el salón hay una mesa y una televisión.

10. ¿Cuántas habitaciones hay en tu casa?

	Time	Mistakes	Referee's name
1			
2			
3			
4			

UNIT 9 – TRAPDOOR

En mi casa En mi piso	hay	cuatro cinco seis siete	habitaciones,	por ejemplo, como	el dormitorio de mis padres mi dormitorio un comedor un cuarto de baño un salón una cocina una sala de juegos

1. In my house, there are five rooms, such as my parents' bedroom.

2. In my flat, there are four rooms. For example, there is a dining room.

3. In my house, there are seven rooms, such as a playroom.

4. In my flat, there are five rooms, such as a bathroom.

5. In my house, there are four rooms, such as my bedroom.

6. In my flat, there are seven rooms. For example, there is a kitchen.

7. In my house, there are five rooms, such as a living room.

8. In my flat, there are six rooms, such as a playroom.

UNIT 9 – COMMUNICATIVE DRILLS

1	2	3
How many rooms are there in your house? - In my house, there are six rooms. For example, there is my bedroom and a living room. **Where do you live?** - I live in a house in the countryside.	**Do you like your house?** - Yes. I like my house because it is clean and well furnished. **What is there in your living room?** - In my living room, there is a sofa, a small table and a television.	**Where do you live?** - I live in a flat in the city centre. **What is there in your flat?** - In my flat, there are four rooms, such as my parents' bedroom and a kitchen.

4	5	6
Do you like your house? - I don't like my house because it is old and ugly. **What is there in your bedroom?** - In my bedroom, there is a wardrobe, a mirror and a bed. **Do you like your house?** - Yes, I like my house because it is cosy.	**What is there in your building?** - In my building, there is a garage and an attic. **Do you live in a flat?** - Yes. I live in a flat on the outskirts. And you? **I live in a house on the coast. I like my house because it is big.**	**Do you like your house?** - Yes. I like my house. **Why?** - I like my house because it is cosy and it is clean. What is there in the kitchen? **In the kitchen, there is a fridge, an oven and a dishwasher.**

UNIT 9 – COMMUNICATIVE DRILLS
REFEREE CARD

1	2	3
¿Cuántas habitaciones hay en tu casa? - En mi casa hay seis habitaciones. Por ejemplo, hay mi dormitorio y un salón. **¿Dónde vives?** - Vivo en una casa en el campo.	**¿Te gusta tu casa?** - Sí. Me gusta mi casa porque está limpia y bien amueblada. **¿Qué hay en tu salón?** - En mi salón hay un sofá, una mesita y una televisión.	**¿Dónde vives?** - Vivo en un piso en el centro de la ciudad. **¿Qué hay en tu piso?** - En mi piso hay cuatro habitaciones, como el dormitorio de mis padres y una cocina.

4	5	6
¿Te gusta tu casa? - No me gusta mi casa porque es antigua y fea. **¿Qué hay en tu dormitorio?** - En mi dormitorio hay un armario, un espejo y una cama. **¿Te gusta tu casa?** - Sí, me gusta mi casa porque es acogedora.	**¿Qué hay en tu edificio?** - En mi edificio hay un garaje y un desván. **¿Vives en un piso?** - Sí. Vivo en un piso en las afueras. ¿Y tú? **Vivo en una casa en la costa. Me gusta mi casa porque es grande.**	**¿Te gusta tu casa?** - Sí. Me gusta mi casa. **¿Por qué?** - Me gusta mi casa porque es acogedora y está limpia. ¿Qué hay en la cocina? **En la cocina hay una nevera, un horno y un lavaplatos.**

UNIT 9 – SURVEY

	¿Cómo te llamas? *What is your name?*	¿Qué hay en tu casa? *What is there in your house?*	¿Cuántas habitaciones hay en tu casa? *How many rooms are there in your house?*	¿Te gusta tu casa? ¿Por qué? *Do you like your house? Why?*	¿Qué hay en la cocina? *What is there in the kitchen?*	¿Qué hay en tu dormitorio? *What is there in your bedroom?*
e.g.	Me llamo Juan.	En mi casa hay una sala de juegos.	En mi casa hay seis habitaciones.	Me gusta mi casa porque es acogedora.	En la cocina hay un horno y una mesa.	En mi dormitorio hay una cama y un escritorio.
1.						
2.						
3.						
4.						
5.						
6.						
7.						

UNIT 9 – ANSWERS

FIND SOMEONE WHO

Find someone who/whose...		Name(s)
1.	...mentions their bathroom.	Louis
2.	...has six rooms in their house, one being a dining room.	Fernando/Belén
3.	...mentions a living room.	Ada
4.	...dislikes their house because it is old.	Rosa
5.	...lives in a building on the coast.	Isabel
6.	...dislikes their house because it is not well furnished.	Patricia
7.	...likes their house because it is cosy.	Raúl
8.	...dislikes their house because it is ugly.	Sonia
9.	...lives in a house on the outskirts.	Ana/Lourdes
10.	...lives in the city centre.	Xavier/Alberto/Rafa
11.	...mentions their parents' bedroom.	Fabio
12.	...is a red herring! (No match)	Paula

STAIRCASE TRANSLATION

Vivo en una casa en el centro de la ciudad. En mi casa hay seis habitaciones. Por ejemplo, hay mi dormitorio y el salón. También hay un desván y un jardín. Me gusta mi casa porque es bonita y luminosa. Sin embargo, está sucia. En la cocina hay un horno. En mi dormitorio hay una cama y un escritorio.

FASTER!

REFEREE SOLUTION:
1. In the living room, there is a television and a sofa.   2. Do you like your house?   3. I live in a flat on the coast.
4. In my house, there are five rooms, such as a playroom.   5. I like my house because it's well lit.
6. I live in a building on the outskirts.   7. In my house, there are six rooms, such as my bedroom.
8. In the kitchen, there is a dishwasher and a chair.   9. In the living room, there is a table and a television.
10. How many rooms are there in your house?

TRAPDOOR

1. En mi casa hay cinco habitaciones, como el dormitorio de mis padres.
2. En mi piso hay cuatro habitaciones. Por ejemplo, hay un comedor.
3. En mi casa hay siete habitaciones, como una sala de juegos.
4. En mi piso hay cinco habitaciones, como un cuarto de baño.
5. En mi casa hay cuatro habitaciones, como mi dormitorio.
6. En mi piso hay siete habitaciones. Por ejemplo, hay una cocina.
7. En mi casa hay cinco habitaciones, como un salón.
8. En mi piso hay seis habitaciones, como una sala de juegos.

THE LANGUAGE GYM

UNIT 10.
Saying what I did in my neighbourhood

¿Adónde fuiste el fin de semana pasado?	Where did you go last weekend?
¿Con quién fuiste?	Who did you go with?
¿Qué hiciste el sábado?	What did you do on Saturday?

Anteayer *The day before yesterday* **Ayer** *Yesterday* **Hace tres días** *Three days ago* **El fin de semana pasado** *Last weekend* **El viernes pasado** *Last Friday*	**compré** *I bought*	**una camiseta de fútbol** *a football shirt* **un videojuego** *a videogame* **ropa nueva** *new clothes*			
	fui *I went*	**a la pista de patinaje** *to the skating rink* **a un concierto de Rosalía** *to a Rosalía concert* **de paseo al parque** *for a walk in the park* **de compras** *shopping*			
	***hice** *I did*	**equitación** *horse riding* **footing** *jogging* **natación** *swimming*		**pesas** *weights* **senderismo** *hiking* **turismo** *sightseeing*	
	jugué *I played*	**al fútbol** **al golf**		**al rugby** **al tenis**	
	toqué *I played (an instrument)*	**el piano** **el violín**		**la batería** *drums* **la guitarra**	
	vi *I watched*	**un espectáculo de circo/danza/magia** *a circus/dance/magic show* **un partido de fútbol** *a football game* **una comedia** *a comedy* **una película de acción/terror** *an action/horror film*			
	visité *I visited*	**un castillo** *a castle* **una galería de arte** *a gallery* **un museo** *a museum*		**un palacio histórico** *a historic palace* **unas ruinas romanas** *some Roman ruins*	

en *in / at*	**el bosque** *the woods* **el campo de fútbol** *the football pitch* **el casco antiguo** *the old town* **el centro comercial** *the shopping mall* **el centro de la ciudad** *the city centre* **el cine** *the cinema* **el club de tenis** *the tennis club* **el estadio** *the stadium* **el polideportivo** *the sports centre* **la calle peatonal** *the pedestrian street* **la piscina (municipal)** *the (local) swimming pool* **la plaza mayor** *the town square*			**cerca de mi casa** *near my house* **de mi barrio** *in my neighbourhood*
con *with*	**mi hermano/a** *my brother/sister* **mi mejor amigo/a** *my best friend*		**mi novio/a** *my boyfriend/girlfriend* **mi primo/a** *my cousin*	

***Author's note:** Watch out for expressions like **"hice natación"** that are translated as *'I went'* swimming. The literal translation is actually *'I did'* swimming. The verbs **"hacer"** and **"ir"** often translate differently in Spanish and English (so watch out for them).

THE LANGUAGE GYM

UNIT 10 – FIND SOMEONE WHO – Student Cards

El viernes pasado jugué al rugby. **OLIVIA**	El fin de semana pasado jugué al tenis. **DAVID**	Ayer visité una galería de arte. **PEPE**	Ayer fui de paseo al parque. **WILLIAM**
Ayer fui a un concierto de Bad Bunny. **SERGIO**	Hace tres días hice senderismo. **PEPITA**	Anteayer fui a la pista de patinaje. **CARLOS**	Hace tres días vi un partido de fútbol. **DANIELA**
Ayer fui de paseo al parque. **GABRIELA**	Anteayer compré una camiseta de fútbol. **ESTHER**	El fin de semana pasado hice turismo. **CARMEN**	Anteayer compré un videojuego. **ANDRÉS**
Anteayer vi una película en el cine. **VÍCTOR**	El viernes pasado visité un museo. **JUANITA**	Ayer visité una galería de arte con mi madre. **GAEL**	Ayer fui a un concierto de Rosalía. **PABLO**

UNIT 10 – FIND SOMEONE WHO – Student Grid

¿Qué hiciste el sábado/viernes/fin de semana pasado/anteayer/ayer?	
What did you do on Saturday/Friday/last weekend/the day before yesterday/yesterday?	
Find someone who...	**Name(s)**
1.	...visited a museum last Friday.	
2.	...played tennis last weekend.	
3.	...went to a concert yesterday.	
4.	...watched a football match three days ago.	
5.	...went for a walk in the park yesterday.	
6.	...bought a football shirt the day before yesterday.	
7.	...played rugby last Friday.	
8.	...bought a videogame the day before yesterday.	
9.	...visited an art gallery yesterday.	
10.	...did hiking three days ago.	
11.	...went to the skating rink the day before yesterday.	
12.	...watched a movie at the cinema the day before yesterday.	
13.	...did sightseeing last weekend.	

THE LANGUAGE GYM

UNIT 10 – ORAL PING-PONG – Person A

ENGLISH	SPANISH	ENGLISH	SPANISH
Yesterday, I visited a museum.	Ayer visité un museo.	Last weekend, I did sightseeing in the old town.	El fin de semana pasado hice turismo en el casco antiguo.
Three days ago, I watched a magic show.		Three days ago, I played tennis at the tennis club in my neighbourhood.	
Yesterday, I watched a film at the cinema with my girlfriend.	Ayer vi una película en el cine con mi novia.	Last Friday, I visited an art gallery in with my best friend (m).	El viernes pasado visité una galería de arte con mi mejor amigo.
The day before yesterday, I went for a walk with my mum.		Last weekend, I did hiking in the woods with my cousin (f).	
Yesterday, I bought new clothes at the shopping mall.	Ayer compré ropa nueva en el centro comercial.	Three days ago, I watched a football match at the stadium with my dad.	Hace tres días vi un partido de fútbol en el estadio con mi padre.
Yesterday, I went jogging in the park.		Three days ago, I bought a football shirt at the shopping mall.	
The day before yesterday, I went to the skating rink with my sister.	Anteayer fui a la pista de patinaje con mi hermana.	The day before yesterday, I visited some Roman ruins with my friend (m).	Anteayer visité unas ruinas romanas con mi amigo.
The day before yesterday, I bought a videogame at the mall.		Last Friday, I went to a Rosalía concert in the stadium with my sister.	
Last Friday, I played football on the football pitch.	El viernes pasado jugué al fútbol en el campo de fútbol.	Last weekend, I played rugby at the sports centre with my friends.	El fin de semana pasado jugué al rugby en el polideportivo con mis amigos.
Three days ago, I visited a historic palace in my neighbourhood.		Yesterday, I watched a circus show in the town square with my family.	

UNIT 10 – ORAL PING-PONG – Person B

ENGLISH	SPANISH	ENGLISH	SPANISH
Yesterday, I visited a museum.		Last weekend, I did sightseeing in the old town.	
Three days ago, I watched a magic show.	Hace tres días vi un espectáculo de magia.	Three days ago, I played tennis at the tennis club in my neighbourhood.	Hace tres días jugué al tenis en el club de tenis de mi barrio.
Yesterday, I watched a film at the cinema with my girlfriend.		Last Friday, I visited an art gallery in with my best friend (m).	
The day before yesterday, I went for a walk with my mum.	Anteayer fui de paseo con mi madre.	Last weekend, I did hiking in the woods with my cousin (f).	El fin de semana pasado hice senderismo en el bosque con mi prima.
Yesterday, I bought new clothes at the shopping mall.		Three days ago, I watched a football match at the stadium with my dad.	
Yesterday, I went jogging in the park.	Ayer hice footing en el parque.	Three days ago, I bought a football shirt at the shopping mall.	Hace tres días compré una camiseta de fútbol en el centro comercial.
The day before yesterday, I went to the skating rink with my sister.		The day before yesterday, I visited some Roman ruins with my friend (m).	
The day before yesterday, I bought a videogame at the mall.	Anteayer compré un videojuego en el centro comercial.	Last Friday, I went to a Rosalía concert in the stadium with my sister.	El viernes pasado fui al concierto de Rosalía en el estadio con mi hermana.
Last Friday, I played football on the football pitch.		Last weekend, I played rugby at the sports centre with my friends.	
Three days ago, I visited a historic palace in my neighbourhood.	Hace tres días visité un palacio histórico en mi barrio.	Yesterday, I watched a circus show in the town square with my family.	Ayer vi un espectáculo de circo en la plaza mayor con mi familia.

THE LANGUAGE GYM

No Snakes No Ladders

7 Yesterday, I went to the cinema in the city centre with my best friend (m).	**6** Last weekend, I went to the park near my house with my dog.	**5** The day before yesterday, I played football on the football pitch in my neighbourhood.	**4** Yesterday, I bought a football shirt at the mall with my sister.	**3** Yesterday, I did sightseeing in the old town with my cousin (m).	**2** Last weekend, I visited an art gallery in the centre with my girlfriend.
8 Where did you go last weekend?	**9** Last Friday, I played tennis at the tennis club with my cousin (m).	**10** Yesterday, I watched a movie at the cinema with my boyfriend.	**11** The day before yesterday, I watched a football match at the stadium with my sister.	**12** Yesterday, I went shopping at the mall with my sister.	**13** What did you do on Saturday?
23 Yesterday, I visited an art gallery in the old town with my best friend (m).	**22** Yesterday, I swam in the local swimming pool with my sister.	**21** Last weekend, I went for a walk on the pedestrian street with my boyfriend.	**20** Yesterday, I did horse riding in the woods with my best friend (f).	**19** What did you do last Friday?	**18** Last Friday, I watched a circus show in the park with my cousin (m).
24 Where did you go the day before yesterday?	**25** Yesterday, I bought a videogame at the shopping mall with my brother.	**26** Three days ago, I did jogging in the park near my house with my dog.	**27** Who did you go with?	**28** Last weekend, I went to the skating rink with my brother.	**29** The day before yesterday, I visited a historic palace in the city centre with my boyfriend.
					30 Yesterday, I bought a gift at the music shop in my neighbourhood with my sister.

1 Three days ago, I visited some Roman ruins in the countryside with my sister.	**14** Last weekend, I went to the local swimming pool with my brother.	**17** Yesterday, I played golf at the park in my neighbourhood with my father.	
START	**15** The day before yesterday, I visited a museum in the city centre with my sister.	**16** Three days ago, I visited a castle on the outskirts of the city with my cousin (f).	**FINISH**

THE LANGUAGE GYM

No Snakes No Ladders

SALIDA	**1** Hace tres días vi unas ruinas romanas en el campo con mi hermana.	**2** El fin de semana pasado visité una galería de arte en el centro con mi novia.	**3** Ayer hice turismo en el casco antiguo con mi primo.	**4** Ayer compré una camiseta de fútbol en el centro comercial con mi hermana.	**5** Anteayer jugué al fútbol en el campo de fútbol de mi barrio.	**6** El fin de semana pasado fui al parque cerca de mi casa con mi perro.	**7** Ayer fui al cine en el centro de la ciudad con mi mejor amigo.
15 Anteayer visité un museo en el centro de la ciudad con mi hermana.	**14** El fin de semana pasado fui a la piscina municipal con mi hermano.	**13** ¿Qué hiciste el sábado?	**12** Ayer fui de compras en el centro comercial con mi hermana.	**11** Anteayer vi un partido de fútbol en el estadio con mi hermana.	**10** Ayer vi una película en el cine con mi novio.	**9** El viernes pasado jugué al tenis en el club de tenis con mi primo.	**8** ¿Adónde fuiste el fin de semana pasado?
16 Hace tres días visité un castillo en las afueras de la ciudad con mi prima.	**17** Ayer jugué al golf en el parque de mi barrio con mi padre.	**18** El viernes pasado vi un espectáculo de circo en el parque con mi primo.	**19** ¿Qué hiciste el viernes pasado?	**20** Ayer hice equitación en el bosque con mi mejor amiga.	**21** El fin de semana pasado fui de paseo por la calle peatonal con mi novio.	**22** Ayer nadé en la piscina municipal con mi hermana.	**23** Ayer visité una galería de arte en el casco antiguo de mi barrio con mi mejor amigo.
LLEGADA	**30** Ayer compré un regalo en la tienda de música de mi barrio con mi hermana.	**29** Anteayer visité un palacio histórico en el centro de la ciudad con mi novio.	**28** El fin de semana pasado fui a la pista de patinaje con mi hermano.	**27** ¿Con quién fuiste?	**26** Hace tres días hice footing en el parque cerca de mi casa con mi perro.	**25** Ayer compré un videojuego en el centro comercial con mi hermano.	**24** ¿Adónde fuiste anteayer?

UNIT 10 – STAIRCASE TRANSLATION

Three days ago, I bought new clothes and a videogame.

Three days ago, I bought new clothes and a videogame in the old town of my neighbourhood.

Three days ago, I bought new clothes and a videogame in the old town of my neighbourhood with my best friend (f) and my brother.

Three days ago, I bought new clothes and a videogame in the old town of my neighbourhood with my best friend (f) and my brother. What did you do last Friday?

Three days ago, I bought new clothes and a videogame in the old town of my neighbourhood with my best friend (f) and my brother. What did you do last Friday? Last weekend, I played tennis at the sports centre.

Three days ago, I bought new clothes and a videogame in the old town of my neighbourhood with my best friend (f) and my brother. What did you do last Friday? Last weekend, I played tennis at the sports centre near my house with my girlfriend.

Translate the last step here:

⏱ UNIT 10 – FASTER! 🐁

Say:

1. Yesterday, I went for a walk in the park.

2. Three days ago, I watched a film at the cinema.

3. Last weekend, I visited the castle in the old town.

4. The day before yesterday, I played football on the football pitch near my house.

5. Last Friday, I did jogging in the woods near my house with my brother.

6. Yesterday, I went to a dance show in the town square of my neighbourhood with my girlfriend.

7. Where did you go last Friday?

8. Last Saturday, I bought a football shirt in the shopping mall near my house with my cousin (m).

	Time	Mistakes	Referee's name
1			
2			
3			
4			

UNIT 10 – THINGS IN COMMON

	1	2	3	4
¿Adónde fuiste el fin de semana pasado?				
¿Qué hiciste el sábado pasado?				
¿Qué hiciste el viernes pasado?				
¿Adónde fuiste ayer?				
¿A qué jugaste el fin de semana pasado?				
¿Qué visitaste ayer?				
¿Qué viste anteayer?				

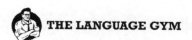

UNIT 10 – COMMUNICATIVE DRILLS

1	2	3
Where did you go yesterday? - Yesterday, I went to the sports centre near my house. **Who did you go with?** - I went with my brother and my sister. The day before yesterday, I visited an art gallery!	**What did you do on Saturday?** - On Saturday, I went for a walk in the park with my best friend (f). Where did you go on Saturday? **Last Saturday, I visited a museum in the city centre.**	**What did you do last weekend?** - Last weekend, I watched a football match at the stadium, I did swimming at the sports centre and I went shopping. And you? **Last Saturday, I visited a historic palace in the old town with my girlfriend.**

4	5	6
What did you do three days ago? - Three days ago, I did hiking in the woods in my neighbourhood. **Who did you go with?** - I went with my boyfriend and my cousin (f).	**What did you do last Friday?** - Last Friday, I watched a film in my neighbourhood cinema with my best friend (m). And you? **Last Friday, I played golf at the park with my brother and I did jogging.**	**Where did you go last Saturday?** - Last Saturday, I went shopping on the pedestrian street near my house. **Who did you go with?** - I went with my girlfriend and my brother.

UNIT 10 – COMMUNICATIVE DRILLS
REFEREE CARD

1	2	3
¿Adónde fuiste ayer? - Ayer fui al polideportivo cerca de mi casa. **¿Con quién fuiste?** - Fui con mi hermano y mi hermana. ¡Anteayer visité una galería de arte!	**¿Qué hiciste el sábado?** - El sábado fui de paseo en el parque con mi mejor amiga. ¿Adónde fuiste el sábado? **El sábado pasado visité un museo en el centro de la ciudad.**	**¿Qué hiciste el fin de semana pasado?** - El fin de semana pasado vi un partido de fútbol en el estadio, nadé en el polideportivo y fui de compras. ¿Y tú? **El sábado pasado visité un palacio histórico en el casco antiguo con mi novia.**

4	5	6
¿Adónde fuiste hace tres días? - Hace tres días hice senderismo en el bosque en mi barrio. **¿Con quién fuiste?** - Fui con mi novio y mi prima.	**¿Qué hiciste el viernes pasado?** - El viernes pasado vi una película en el cine en mi barrio con mi mejor amigo. ¿Y tú? **El viernes pasado jugué al golf en el parque con mi hermano e hice footing.**	**¿Adónde fuiste el sábado pasado?** - El sábado pasado fui de compras en la calle peatonal cerca de mi casa. **¿Con quién fuiste?** - Fui con mi novia y mi hermano.

UNIT 10 – SURVEY

	¿Cómo te llamas? *What is your name?*	¿Adónde fuiste el fin de semana pasado? *Where did you go last weekend?*	¿Qué hiciste el viernes pasado? *What did you do last Friday?*	¿A qué jugaste ayer? *What did you play yesterday?*	¿Qué visitaste ayer? *What did you visit yesterday?*	¿Qué viste el fin de semana pasado? *What did you watch last weekend?*
e.g.	Me llamo Juan.	El fin de semana pasado fui al parque.	El viernes pasado compré ropa nueva.	Ayer jugué al tenis en el club de tenis.	Ayer visité una galería de arte.	El fin de semana pasado vi una película en el cine.
1.						
2.						
3.						
4.						
5.						
6.						
7.						

UNIT 10 – ANSWERS

FIND SOMEONE WHO

Find someone who...	Name(s)
1. ...visited a museum last Friday.	Juanita
2. ...played tennis last weekend.	David
3. ...went to a concert yesterday.	Sergio/Pablo
4. ...watched a football match three days ago.	Daniela
5. ...went for a walk in the park yesterday.	William/Gabriela
6. ...bought a football shirt the day before yesterday.	Esther
7. ...played rugby last Friday.	Olivia
8. ...bought a videogame the day before yesterday.	Andrés
9. ...visited an art gallery yesterday.	Pepe/Gael
10. ...did hiking three days ago.	Pepita
11. ...went to the skating rink the day before yesterday.	Carlos
12. ...watched a movie at the cinema the day before yesterday.	Víctor
13. ...did sightseeing last weekend.	Carmen

STAIRCASE TRANSLATION

Hace tres días compré ropa nueva y un videojuego en el casco antiguo de mi barrio con mi mejor amiga y mi hermano. ¿Qué hiciste el viernes pasado? El fin de semana pasado jugué al tenis en el polideportivo cerca de mi casa con mi novia.

FASTER!

REFEREE SOLUTION:

1. Ayer fui de paseo en el parque.   2. Hace tres días vi una película en el cine.

3. El fin de semana pasado visité el castillo en el casco antiguo.

4. Anteayer jugué al fútbol en el campo de fútbol cerca de mi casa.

5. El viernes pasado hice footing en el bosque cerca de mi casa con mi hermano.

6. Ayer fui a un espectáculo de danza en la plaza mayor de mi barrio con mi novia.

7. ¿Adónde fuiste el viernes pasado?

8. El sábado pasado compré una camiseta de fútbol en el centro comercial cerca de mi casa con mi primo.

THINGS IN COMMON

Students give their own answers to the questions and make a note of which students they have things in common with.

UNIT 11.
Saying what I did & am going to do at the weekend

INSTRUCTIONS FOR ALL GAMES ARE ON PAGES 1-2

¿Qué hiciste el fin de semana pasado?	What did you do last weekend?
¿Cómo fue?	How was it?
¿Qué vas a hacer el próximo fin de semana?	What are you going to do next weekend?
¿Qué va a hacer tu hermano/a?	What is your brother/sister going to do?

El fin de semana pasado *Last weekend*	yo	fui / fuimos	*I went / we went*	a casa de mi amigo/a / al estadio	*to my friend's house / to the stadium*
	mi amigo/a y yo *my friend and I*	hice / hicimos	*I did / we did*	deporte / mis deberes	*sport / homework*
El viernes pasado *Last Friday*	nosotros *we – (m / mixed)*	jugué / jugamos	*I played / we played*	a videojuegos / en mi ordenador	*videogames / on my computer*
El domingo pasado *Last Sunday*	nosotras *we (f)*	toqué / tocamos	*I played / we played*	el piano / la guitarra	*piano / guitar*
		vi / vimos	*I saw / we saw*	un partido de fútbol / una película	*a football match / a flim*

Fue *It was*	bastante un poco muy	aburrido *boring* divertido *fun* interesante
No fue nada *It was not … at all*		

El próximo fin de semana *Next weekend*	voy a *I am going*	hacer *to do*	deporte / los deberes	*sport*
		ir *to go*	a una fiesta / al centro comercial / de compras	*to a party / to the shopping mall / shopping*
El próximo sábado *Next Saturday*	mi hermana va a *my sister is going*	jugar *to play*	al baloncesto / en mi ordenador	*basketball / on my computer*
	mi hermano y yo vamos a *my brother and I are going*	tocar *to play*	la batería	*drums*
El próximo domingo *Next Sunday*	mis padres van a *my parents are going*	ver *to see*	un concierto / un partido de fútbol / una película	*a concert / a football match / a film*

Será *It will be*	bastante *quite* un poco *a bit* muy *very*	agotador *exhausting* apasionante *exciting* guay *cool*
No será nada *It won't be … at all*		

Author's notes:

1) **Nosotros** is the personal pronoun for "we". You use it when talking about a male or mixed gender group (regardless of the ratio of girls and boys). **Nosotras** is "we" for an all girl group.

2) Don't forget there are two verbs to say "I play": **tocar** (for instruments) and **jugar** (for sports)

UNIT 11 – FIND SOMEONE WHO – Student Cards

El fin de semana pasado vimos un partido de fútbol. **MIRABEL**	El próximo sábado mi hermana va a ir a una fiesta. **JULIO**	El próximo domingo mis padres van a ir a una fiesta. **LUCAS**	El fin de semana pasado vimos una película en casa. **JESSE**
El viernes pasado toqué la guitarra. **ANTONIO**	El próximo domingo mis padres van a hacer deporte. **CAMILO**	El domingo pasado hice mis deberes en el salón. **JORGE**	El viernes pasado mi amigo y yo jugamos al fútbol. **DAVID**
El domingo pasado jugamos a videojuegos. **FRAN**	El viernes pasado yo fui a casa de mi amigo. **JUAN**	El domingo pasado tocamos el piano. **CECIL**	El próximo fin de semana mi hermano y yo vamos a ver un partido de fútbol. **SAMUEL**
El próximo fin de semana voy a ir al centro comercial. **BRUNO**	El domingo pasado hice mis deberes. **ALBA**	El viernes pasado toqué la guitarra en mi dormitorio. **HARRIET**	El próximo fin de semana voy a ir al centro comercial. **STEFANO**

UNIT 11 – FIND SOMEONE WHO – Student Grid

¿Qué hiciste el fin de semana pasado?	*What did you do last weekend?*	
¿Qué hiciste el viernes pasado?	*What did you do last Friday?*	
¿Qué vas a hacer el próximo fin de semana?	*What are you going to do next weekend?*	

	Find someone who...	Name(s)
1.	...has parents who are going to do sport next Sunday.	
2.	...has a sister who is going to a party next Saturday.	
3.	...played the piano last Sunday.	
4.	...played guitar last Friday.	
5.	...played videogames last Sunday.	
6.	...is going to watch a football match next weekend.	
7.	...went to their friend's house last Friday.	
8.	...watched a movie at home last weekend.	
9.	...is going to the shopping mall next weekend.	
10.	...did homework last Sunday.	
11.	...has parents who are going to a party next Sunday.	
12.	...played football last Friday.	
13.	...watched a football match last weekend.	

UNIT 11 – ORAL PING-PONG – Person A

ENGLISH	SPANISH	ENGLISH	SPANISH
Last weekend, we went to the stadium.	El fin de semana pasado fuimos al estadio.	What are you going to do next weekend?	¿Qué vas a hacer el próximo fin de semana?
Last Friday, I played videogames on my computer.		Next Sunday, my sister is going to play on my computer.	
It wasn't fun at all.	No fue nada divertido.	Next weekend, I'm going to watch a movie.	El próximo fin de semana voy a ver una película.
Next weekend, I'm going to play basketball.		It was a bit boring.	
Next Saturday, I'm going to do my homework.	El próximo sábado voy a hacer los deberes.	Next weekend, my brother and I are going to watch a football match.	El próximo fin de semana mi hermano y yo vamos a ver un partido de fútbol.
What did you do last weekend?		Next Sunday, my parents are going to a party.	
Next Sunday, my sister is going to do sport.	El próximo domingo mi hermana va a hacer deporte.	Last Friday, my friends and I did sport.	El viernes pasado mis amigos y yo hicimos deporte.
Last Friday, we went to the stadium.		Last Sunday, we went to my friend's house.	
Last weekend, we did homework.	El fin de semana pasado hicimos los deberes.	It won't be exciting at all.	No será nada apasionante.
It will be a bit exhausting.		Last weekend, we did sport.	

UNIT 11 – ORAL PING-PONG – Person B

ENGLISH	SPANISH	ENGLISH	SPANISH
Last weekend, we went to the stadium.		What are you going to do next weekend?	
Last Friday, I played videogames on my computer.	El viernes pasado jugué a videojuegos en mi ordenador.	Next Sunday, my sister is going to play on my computer.	El próximo domingo mi hermana va a jugar en mi ordenador.
It wasn't fun at all.		Next weekend, I'm going to watch a movie.	
Next weekend, I'm going to play basketball.	El próximo fin de semana voy a jugar al baloncesto.	It was a bit boring.	Fue un poco aburrido.
Next Saturday, I'm going to do homework.		Next weekend, my brother and I are going to watch a football match.	
What did you do last weekend?	¿Qué hiciste el fin de semana pasado?	Next Sunday, my parents are going to a party.	El próximo domingo mis padres van a ir a una fiesta.
Next Sunday, my sister is going to do sport.		Last Friday, my friends and I did sport.	
Last Friday, we went to the stadium.	El viernes pasado fuimos al estadio.	Last Sunday, we went to my friend's house.	El domingo pasado fuimos a casa de mi amigo.
Last weekend, we did homework.		It won't be exciting at all.	
It will be a bit exhausting.	Será un poco agotador.	Last weekend, we did sport.	El fin de semana pasado hicimos deporte.

No Snakes No Ladders

START	**1** Last Sunday, I played guitar.	**2** Last weekend, we played football.	**3** Next Sunday, my sister is going to play piano.	**4** Next Saturday, my brother and I are going to play basketball.	**5** Next weekend, I'm going to go to the shopping mall.	**6** It wasn't fun at all.	**7** What did you do last weekend?
15 Next Saturday, we're going to play the drums.	**14** Last Friday, my friends and I did sport.	**13** Next weekend, we're going to do homework.	**12** It will be quite cool.	**11** Last Sunday, I watched a football match.	**10** Next Sunday, we're going to go to a party.	**9** Last weekend, we went to the stadium.	**8** Next Saturday, my parents are going shopping.
16 Last Friday, we did homework.	**17** It will be very exciting.	**18** Last Friday, I played videogames on my computer.	**19** Last Sunday, I watched a movie.	**20** Next Sunday, I'm going to watch a movie at the cinema.	**21** How was it?	**22** Next weekend, we're going to go to a concert.	**23** Next Saturday, my parents are going to do sport.
FINISH	**30** Next Saturday, we're going to watch a football match.	**29** What is your brother going to do?	**28** Last Sunday, I went to my friend's house.	**27** Last Saturday, we did sport.	**26** Next Saturday, I'm going to watch a football match.	**25** It was very interesting.	**24** Last Sunday, we played videogames on my computer.

THE LANGUAGE GYM

127

No Snakes No Ladders

7 ¿Qué hiciste el fin de semana pasado?	**6** No fue nada divertido.	**5** El próximo fin de semana voy a ir al centro comercial.	**4** El próximo sábado mi hermano y yo vamos a jugar al baloncesto.	**3** El próximo domingo mi hermana va a tocar el piano.	**2** El fin de semana pasado jugamos al fútbol.
8 El próximo sábado mis padres van a ir de compras.	**9** El fin de semana pasado fuimos al estadio.	**10** El próximo domingo vamos a ir a una fiesta.	**11** El domingo pasado yo vi un partido de fútbol.	**12** Será bastante guay.	**13** El próximo fin de semana vamos a hacer los deberes.
23 El próximo sábado mis padres van a hacer deporte.	**22** El próximo fin de semana vamos a ir a un concierto.	**21** ¿Cómo fue?	**20** El próximo domingo voy a ver una película en el cine.	**19** El domingo pasado yo vi una película.	**18** El viernes pasado jugué a videojuegos en mi ordenador.
24 El domingo pasado jugamos a videojuegos en mi ordenador.	**25** Fue muy interesante.	**26** El próximo sábado voy a ver un partido de fútbol.	**27** El sábado pasado nosotras hicimos deporte.	**28** El domingo pasado yo fui a casa de mi amigo.	**29** ¿Qué va a hacer tu hermano?

1 El domingo pasado toqué la guitarra.	**SALIDA**	
14 El viernes pasado mis amigos y yo hicimos deporte.	**13** El próximo fin de semana vamos a hacer los deberes.	
17 Será muy apasionante.	**16** El viernes pasado nosotros hicimos los deberes.	**15** El próximo sábado vamos a tocar la batería.
30 El próximo sábado vamos a ver un partido de fútbol.	**LLEGADA**	

THE LANGUAGE GYM

UNIT 11 – STAIRCASE TRANSLATION

Last weekend, I watched a football match.

Last weekend, I watched a football match. It was quite fun.

Last weekend, I watched a football match. It was quite fun. Next Saturday, my brother and I are going to go to a party.

Last weekend, I watched a football match. It was quite fun. Next Saturday, my brother and I are going to go to a party. Next Sunday, I'm going to do my homework.

Last weekend, I watched a football match. It was quite fun. Next Saturday, my brother and I are going to go to a party. Next Sunday, I'm going to do my homework. It will be very exhausting.

Last weekend, I watched a football match. It was quite fun. Next Saturday, my brother and I are going to go to a party. Next Sunday, I'm going to do my homework. It will be very exhausting. What are you going to do next weekend ?

Translate the last step here :

⏱ UNIT 11 – FASTER! 🐦

Say:

1. Last weekend, I did sport.

2. Next Saturday, I'm going to go shopping.

3. It will be quite exciting.

4. Last Sunday, we watched a football match.

5. Last Friday, my friend and I played videogames.

6. Next Saturday, my sister is going to go to a concert.

7. It was not fun at all.

8. What are you going to do this weekend?

9. It will be very cool and interesting.

10. Next Sunday, my parents are going to go to a party.

	Time	Mistakes	Referee's name
1			
2			
3			
4			

UNIT 11 – FLUENCY CARDS

Next weekend, I…		
Last Sunday, we…		
Last Friday, my friend and I…		
Next Saturday, my sister…		
Last Sunday, I…		
Next weekend, I…		

	Time	Mistakes
1		
2		
3		
4		

UNIT 11 – COMMUNICATIVE DRILLS

1	2	3
What did you do last weekend? - Last weekend, I went to my friend's house. **How was it?** - It was quite fun. It wasn't boring at all.	**What are you going to do next Saturday?** - Next Saturday, my brother and I are going to play basketball. It will be very exhausting. What are you going to do next weekend? **I am going to do my homework.**	**What is your brother going to do next Saturday?** - Next Saturday, my brother is going to watch a football match. Do you have a brother? **Yes, I have a brother. Next Saturday, my brother and I are going to watch a film.**
4	5	6
What did you do last Sunday? - Last Sunday, we went to the stadium. **How was it?** - We watched a football match and it was very exciting. Next Sunday, we are going to play basketball.	**What are you going to do next Sunday?** - Next Sunday, my parents and I are going to go to the shopping mall. We are going to go shopping and watch a film. And you? **Next Sunday, my sister and I are going to do homework. It will be very boring.**	**What are you going to do next weekend?** - Next weekend, I am going to play the drums and go to a concert. **What is your sister going to do?** - My sister is going to go shopping.
7	8	9
Last weekend, my friend and I played videogames. What did you do last weekend? - Last weekend, we did sport. It was quite exhausting. What are you going to do next Friday? **Next Friday, my sister and I are going to go to a party. It will be cool.**	**Last Friday, I went to a party.** - How was it? **It was not fun at all. What are you going to do next weekend?** - Next Saturday, I am going to do sport. Next Sunday, I'm going to go to a concert. It will be exhausting!	**What is your sister going to do next Friday?** - Next Friday, my sister is going to go to the shopping mall. She is going to go shopping. And you? **Next Friday, I'm going do hiking because I went shopping last Friday.**

1	2	3
¿Qué hiciste el fin de semana pasado? - El fin de semana pasado fui a casa de mi amigo. **¿Cómo fue?** - Fue bastante divertido. No fue nada aburrido.	**¿Qué vas a hacer el próximo sábado?** - El próximo sábado mi hermano y yo vamos a jugar al baloncesto. Será muy agotador. ¿Qué vas a hacer el próximo fin de semana? **Voy a hacer mis deberes.**	**¿Qué va a hacer tu hermano el próximo sábado?** - El próximo sábado mi hermano va a ver un partido de fútbol. ¿Tienes un hermano? **Sí, tengo un hermano. El próximo sábado mi hermano y yo vamos a ver una película.**

4	5	6
¿Qué hiciste el domingo pasado? - El domingo pasado fuimos al estadio. **¿Cómo fue?** - Vimos un partido de fútbol y fue muy apasionante. El próximo domingo vamos a jugar al baloncesto.	**¿Qué vas a hacer el próximo domingo?** - El próximo domingo mis padres y yo vamos a ir al centro comercial. Vamos a ir de compras y ver una película. ¿Y tú? **El próximo domingo mi hermana y yo vamos a hacer los deberes. Será muy aburrido.**	**¿Qué vas a hacer el próximo fin de semana?** - El próximo fin de semana voy a tocar la batería e ir a un concierto. **¿Qué va a hacer tu hermana?** Mi hermana va a ir de compras.

7	8	9
El fin de semana pasado mi amigo y yo jugamos a videojuegos. ¿Qué hiciste el fin de semana pasado? - El fin de semana pasado hicimos deporte. Fue bastante agotador. ¿Qué vas a hacer el próximo viernes? **El próximo viernes mi hermana y yo vamos a ir a una fiesta. Será guay.**	**El viernes pasado fui a una fiesta.** - ¿Cómo fue? **No fue nada divertido. ¿Qué vas a hacer el próximo fin de semana?** - El próximo sábado voy a hacer deporte. El próximo domingo voy a ir a un concierto. ¡Será agotador!	**¿Qué va a hacer tu hermana el próximo viernes?** - El próximo viernes mi hermana va a ir al centro comercial. Va a ir de compras. ¿Y tú? **El próximo viernes voy a hacer senderismo porque fui de compras el viernes pasado.**

UNIT 11 – SURVEY

	¿Cómo te llamas? *What is your name?*	¿Qué hiciste el fin de semana pasado? *What did you do last weekend?*	¿Cómo fue? *How was it?*	¿Qué vas a hacer el próximo sábado? *What are you going to do next Saturday?*	¿Qué vas a hacer el próximo domingo? *What are you going to do next Sunday?*
e.g.	Me llamo Gonzalo.	El fin de semana pasado hice deporte.	Fue muy agotador.	El próximo sábado voy a tocar la batería.	El próximo domingo voy a ir de compras.
1.					
2.					
3.					
4.					
5.					
6.					
7.					

UNIT 11 – ANSWERS

FIND SOMEONE WHO

Find someone who...	Name(s)
1. ...has parents who are going to do sport next Sunday.	Camilo
2. ...has a sister who is going to a party next Saturday.	Julio
3. ...played the piano last Sunday.	Cecil
4. ...played guitar last Friday.	Antonio/Harriet
5. ...played videogames last Sunday.	Fran
6. ...is going to watch a football match next weekend.	Samuel
7. ...went to their friend's house last Friday.	Juan
8. ...watched a movie at home last weekend.	Jesse
9. ...is going to the shopping mall next weekend.	Bruno/Stefano
10. ...did homework last Sunday.	Alba/Jorge
11. ...has parents who are going to a party next Sunday.	Lucas
12. ...played football last Friday.	David
13. ...watched a football match last weekend.	Mirabel

STAIRCASE TRANSLATION

El fin de semana pasado vi un partido de fútbol. Fue bastante divertido. El próximo sábado mi hermano y yo vamos a ir a una fiesta. El próximo domingo voy a hacer mis deberes. Será muy agotador. ¿Qué vas a hacer el próximo fin de semana?

FASTER!

REFEREE SOLUTION:

1. El fin de semana pasado hice deporte.   2. El próximo sábado voy a ir de compras.
3. Será bastante emocionante.   4. El domingo pasado vimos un partido de fútbol.
5. El viernes pasado mi amigo y yo jugamos a videojuegos.
6. El próximo sábado mi hermana va a ir a un concierto.   7. No fue nada divertido.
8. ¿Qué vas a hacer este fin de semana?   9. Será muy guay e interesante.
10. El próximo domingo mis padres van a ir a una fiesta.

FLUENCY CARDS

1. El próximo fin de semana voy a jugar a videojuegos en mi ordenador.
2. El domingo pasado tocamos la guitarra y vimos una película.
3. El viernes pasado mi amigo y yo hicimos deporte y fuimos de compras.
4. El próximo sábado mi hermana va a hacer los deberes y ver un partido de fútbol / jugar al fútbol.
5. El domingo pasado jugué al baloncesto y toqué el piano.
6. El próximo fin de semana voy a ir a casa de un amigo e ir a una fiesta.

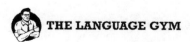
THE LANGUAGE GYM

¿Qué quieres *What do you want* ¿Qué te gustaría *What would you like*	hacer *to do*	esta mañana? *this morning?* esta tarde? *this afternoon?* este fin de semana? *this weekend?*		hoy? *today?* mañana? *tomorrow?*

Hoy	*me apetece *I fancy 'to'* me gustaría *I would like to* quiero *I want to*	dar una vuelta en bici *go for a bike ride* ir al cine *go to the cinema* ir de tiendas *go shopping* jugar al baloncesto *play basketball*	

¿Te gustaría *Would you like to*	dar una vuelta *go for a walk* ir a casa de Pablo *go to Pablo's house* ir al parque *go to the park* jugar a la Play *play on the PlayStation*	conmigo? *with me?* juntos? *together?*

Lo siento, *Sorry,*		no me apetece *I don't fancy it* no tengo ganas *I don't feel like it*	no quiero *I don't want to*
Bueno, *Well,*	me apetece, pero *I fancy it, but* me gustaría, pero *I would like to, but*	no puedo *I can't*	
		tengo que *I have to*	ayudar a mi madre/padre *help my mum/dad* estudiar *study* hacer las tareas domésticas *do the chores* ir a casa de mis abuelos *go to my grandparents' house* trabajar *work*
Sí, me apetece *Yes, I fancy it*		¡Qué guay! *(How) Great!*	

Está bien *It's fine* No pasa nada *No problem* Vale *OK*	podemos *we can*	ir a casa de Pablo *go to Pablo's house* ir al estadio *go to the stadium* jugar a la consola *play on the games console* quedarnos en casa *stay at home*

¡Fantástico! *Fantastic!* ¡Genial! *Great!*	¿A qué hora *At what time* ¿Dónde *Where*	quedamos? *shall we meet?*

Quedamos *Let's meet* Vamos a quedar *We are going to meet*	enfrente *opposite*	de la casa de Paco *Paco's house* del centro comercial *the shopping mall* del cine *the cinema*	a las *at*	cinco seis siete	y cuarto y media menos diez
Genial, nos vemos luego *Great, we'll see each other later*			Hasta luego *See you later*		

*Author's note: In Spanish, we use "me apetece" to say that we fancy doing something. It can be used in the same way as "me gusta" or "me gustaría", followed by an infinitive.

THE LANGUAGE GYM

UNIT 12 – FIND SOMEONE WHO – Student Cards

Hoy me gustaría ir al cine. **DIEGO**	Quiero dar una vuelta en el centro. **HARRIET**	Esta mañana me apetece ir de tiendas. **GABRIELA**	Hoy me apetece ir al parque. **SERGIO**
Tengo que hacer las tareas domésticas. **CARLOS**	Esta mañana tengo que jugar a la consola. **JULIÁN**	Quiero ir a casa de mis abuelos. **VICTORIA**	Hoy quiero ayudar a mi madre. **AMPARO**
Esta tarde tengo que ir a casa de Pablo. **PALOMA**	Hoy me apetece ir al parque. **JULIA**	Me gustaría ir al estadio. **MIGUEL**	Hoy quiero jugar al baloncesto. **PABLO**
Hoy quiero jugar al baloncesto en el parque. **JOSÉ**	Esta tarde me gustaría jugar a la consola. **AURORA**	Hoy quiero ayudar a mi madre. **CATALINA**	Esta tarde tengo que trabajar. **FELIPE**

UNIT 12 – FIND SOMEONE WHO – Student Grid

¿Qué te gustaría hacer hoy?	*What would you like to do today?*	
Find someone who...		**Name(s)**
1.	...wants to play basketball today.	
2.	...would like to go to the stadium today.	
3.	...has to go to Pablo's house this afternoon.	
4.	...fancies going to the park today.	
5.	...wants to go to their grandparents' house.	
6.	...wants to go for a walk in the city centre.	
7.	...wants to go to the cinema today.	
8.	...has to work this afternoon.	
9.	...has to do household chores today.	
10.	...fancies going shopping this morning.	
11.	...would like to play on the games console this afternoon.	
12.	...wants to help their mum today.	
13.	...is a red herring! 🐟 (No match)	

UNIT 12 – ORAL PING-PONG – Person A

ENGLISH	SPANISH	ENGLISH	SPANISH
What do you want to do this weekend?	¿Qué quieres hacer este fin de semana?	**Well, I fancy it, but I have to work.**	Bueno, me apetece, pero tengo que trabajar.
Would you like to go to Pablo's house with me?		**No problem, we can stay at home.**	
Well, I would like to, but I have to help my father.	Bueno, me gustaría, pero tengo que ayudar a mi padre.	**Today, I would like to play basketball.**	Hoy me gustaría jugar al baloncesto.
Today, I want to go shopping.		**What would I like to do today?**	
What would you like to do this afternoon?	¿Qué te gustaría hacer esta tarde?	**Well, I would like to, but I have to go to my grandparents' house.**	Bueno, me gustaría, pero tengo que ir a casa de mis abuelos.
It's fine, we can go to Pablo's house.		**I fancy it today, but I have to study.**	
Today I would like to go to the cinema.	Hoy me gustaría ir al cine.	**Yes, I fancy it. How cool!**	Sí, me apetece. ¡Qué guay!
Let's meet opposite the cinema at 6:30.		**We are going to meet opposite the shopping mall at 5:00.**	
Today, I fancy going for a bike ride.	Hoy me apetece dar una vuelta en bici.	**Well, I fancy it, but I have to help my mother.**	Bueno, me apetece, pero tengo que ayudar a mi madre.
Would you like to play on the games console together?		**Let's meet opposite Paco's house at 4:50**	

UNIT 12 – ORAL PING-PONG – Person B

ENGLISH	SPANISH	ENGLISH	SPANISH
What do you want to do this weekend?		Well, I fancy it, but I have to work.	
Would you like to go to Pablo's house with me?	¿Te gustaría ir a casa de Pablo conmigo?	No problem, we can stay at home.	No pasa nada, podemos quedarnos en casa.
Well, I would like to, but I have to help my father.		Today, I would like to play basketball.	
Today, I want to go shopping.	Hoy quiero ir de tiendas.	What would I like to do today?	¿Qué te gustaría hacer hoy?
What would you like to do this afternoon?		Well, I would like to, but I have to go to my grandparents' house.	
It's fine, we can go to Pablo's house.	Está bien, podemos ir a casa de Pablo.	I fancy it today, but I have to study.	Hoy me apetece, pero tengo que estudiar.
Today I would like to go to the cinema.		Yes, I fancy it. How cool!	
Let's meet opposite the cinema at 6:30.	Quedamos enfrente del cine a las seis y media.	We are going to meet opposite the shopping mall at 5:00.	Vamos a quedar enfrente del centro comercial a las cinco.
Today, I fancy going for a bike ride.		Well, I fancy it, but I have to help my mother.	
Would you like to play on the games console together?	¿Te gustaría jugar a la consola juntos?	Let's meet opposite Paco's house at 4:50	Quedamos enfrente de la casa de Paco a las cinco menos diez.

No Snakes No Ladders

START

1	Let's meet in front of the shopping centre at 7:00.
2	What would you like to do this afternoon?
3	Would you like to go to Pablo's house with me?
4	Today, I want to go shopping.
5	Well, I fancy it, but I have to work.
6	Today, I would like to go to the cinema.
7	What would you like to do today?
8	Would you like to play on the PlayStation together?
9	Well, I fancy it, but I have to go to my grandparents' house.
10	Okay, we can play on the PlayStation.
11	Would you like to go to the shopping centre with me?
12	Fantastic! What time shall we meet?
13	No problem, we can stay at home.
14	Today, I would like to play basketball.
15	It's fine, we can go to Pablo's house.
16	Today, I would like to go shopping.
17	See you later.
18	Great, we'll see each other later.
19	We're going to meet opposite the cinema at 7:15.
20	Well, I fancy it, but I can't.
21	We are going to meet opposite the shopping mall at 5:00.
22	Yes, I fancy it. Great!
23	Well, I fancy it, but I have to help my mum.
24	Sorry, I don't want to.
25	No problem, we can play on the games console.
26	Well, I would like to, but I have to study.
27	Let's meet opposite Paco's house at 5:00.
28	I fancy it today, but I have to study.
29	It's fine, we can go to the stadium.
30	Okay, we can stay at home.

FINISH

No Snakes No Ladders

7 ¿Qué te gustaría hacer hoy?	**8** ¿Te gustaría jugar a la Play juntos?	**23** Bueno, me apetece, pero tengo que ayudar a mi madre.	**24** Lo siento, no quiero.			
6 Hoy me gustaría ir al cine.	**9** Bueno, me apetece, pero tengo que ir a casa de mis abuelos.	**22** Sí, me apetece. ¡Genial!	**25** No pasa nada, podemos jugar a la consola.			
5 Bueno, me apetece, pero tengo que trabajar.	**10** Vale, podemos jugar a la Play.	**21** Vamos a quedar enfrente del centro comercial a las cinco.	**26** Bueno, me gustaría, pero tengo que estudiar.			
4 Hoy quiero ir de tiendas.	**11** ¿Te gustaría ir al centro comercial conmigo?	**20** Bueno, me apetece, pero no puedo.	**27** Quedamos enfrente de la casa de Paco a las cinco.			
3 ¿Te gustaría ir a casa de Pablo conmigo?	**12** ¡Fantástico! ¿A qué hora quedamos?	**19** Vamos a quedar enfrente del cine a las siete y cuarto.	**28** Hoy me apetece, pero tengo que estudiar.			
2 ¿Qué te gustaría hacer esta tarde?	**13** No pasa nada, podemos quedarnos en casa.	**18** Genial, nos vemos luego.	**29** Está bien, podemos ir al estadio.			
1 Quedamos enfrente del centro comercial a las siete.	**14** Hoy me gustaría jugar al baloncesto.	**17** Hasta luego.	**30** Vale, podemos quedarnos en casa.			
SALIDA	**15** Está bien, podemos ir a casa de Pablo.	**16** Hoy me gustaría ir de tiendas.	**LLEGADA**			

THE LANGUAGE GYM

UNIT 12 – STAIRCASE TRANSLATION

What do you want to do today ?

What do you want to do today ? Today, I would like to go shopping.

What do you want to do today ? Today, I would like to go shopping. Would you like to go to the park with me ?

What do you want to do today ? Today, I would like to go shopping. Would you like to go to the park with me ? Well, I fancy it, but I have to help my mum.

What do you want to do today ? Today, I would like to go shopping. Would you like to go to the park with me ? Well, I fancy it, but I have to help my mum. It's fine, we can stay at home.

What do you want to do today ? Today, I would like to go shopping. Would you like to go to the park with me ? Well, I fancy it, but I have to help my mum. It's fine, we can stay at home. Where shall we meet ? Let's meet opposite the cinema at 6 :30.

Translate the last step here :

⏱ UNIT 12 – FASTER! 💨

Say:

1. Today, I want to play basketball.

2. I'm sorry, I don't fancy it.

3. It's fine, we can play on the PlayStation.

4. Well, I would like to, but I have to work.

5. Great! Where shall we meet?

6. What do you want to do this afternoon?

7. Would you like to go to Pablo's house with me?

8. Today, I would like to go for a bike ride.

9. We are going to meet opposite the cinema at 5:30.

10. Well, I fancy it, but I have to do the chores.

	Time	Mistakes	Referee's name
1			
2			
3			
4			

UNIT 12 – FAST & FURIOUS

1. Hoy _____ _____ dar una vuelta en bici.   (I fancy)

2. _____ _____ ir a casa de mis abuelos.   (I would like)

3. Hoy _____ ir al parque, pero tengo que estudiar.   (I want)

4. Hoy quiero _____ a la Play.   (to play)

5. Está bien, podemos _____ al estadio.   (to go)

6. Bueno, me apetece, pero tengo que _____ a mi padre.   (to help)

7. Vamos a _____ enfrente del cine.   (to meet)

8. ¿Qué quieres _____ esta tarde?   (to do)

9. Lo siento, no _____.   (I can)

10. ¡Fantástico! ¿A qué hora _____?   (we meet)

	Time 1	Time 2	Time 3	Time 4
Time				
Mistakes				

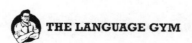

UNIT 12 – COMMUNICATIVE DRILLS

1	2	3
What do you want to do this weekend? - I fancy going shopping and going for a bike ride. **What would you like to do tomorrow?** - Tomorrow, I want to play basketball.	**Would you like to go to the park together?** - Yes, I fancy it. **Ok, we can go to the park.** - What time shall we meet? **Let's meet opposite my house at 6:00.**	**What do you want to do this afternoon?** - This afternoon, I want to play on the PlayStation. Would you like to play on the PlayStation with me? **Well, I fancy it, but I have to go to my grandparents' house.** - No problem.

4	5	6
Would you like to study tomorrow? - Sorry, I don't fancy it. Would you like to go to the stadium? **Well, I would like to, but I have to study.** - Ok, we can stay at home and study.	**Today, I fancy going to the cinema. Do you want to come with me?** - Yes, I fancy it. How cool! What time shall we meet? **We are going to meet opposite the cinema at 5:15.** - Fantastic! See you later.	**Would you like to do the chores?** - Well, I fancy it, but I have to work. **It's fine. Would you like to work together?** - Ok. Where shall we meet? **Let's meet opposite the shopping mall.**

7	8	9
Do you want to go shopping with me? - Yes, I fancy it. Great! What time shall we meet? **We are going to meet opposite the shopping centre at 6:50.** - It's fine. We'll see each other later.	**Would you like to go to my grandparents' house with me?** - Well, I fancy it, but I can't. **Why not?** - I have to help my dad and study. **Ok. That's fine.**	**What would you like to do tomorrow?** - Tomorrow, I have to go to Pablo's house. **Would you like to go for a walk in the centre with me?** - Yes, I'd like to. **Ok, see you tomorrow.**

UNIT 12 – COMMUNICATIVE DRILLS
REFEREE CARD

1	2	3
¿Qué quieres hacer este fin de semana? - Me apetece ir de tiendas y dar una vuelta en bici. **¿Qué te gustaría hacer mañana?** - Mañana quiero jugar al baloncesto.	**¿Te gustaría ir al parque juntos?** - Sí, me apetece. **Vale, podemos ir al parque.** - ¿A qué hora quedamos? **Quedamos enfrente de mi casa a las seis.**	**¿Qué quieres hacer esta tarde?** - Esta tarde quiero jugar a la Play. ¿Te gustaría jugar a la Play conmigo? **Bueno, me apetece, pero tengo que ir a casa de mis abuelos.** - No pasa nada.

4	5	6
¿Te gustaría estudiar mañana? - Lo siento, no me apetece. ¿Te gustaría ir al estadio? **Bueno, me gustaría, pero tengo que estudiar.** - Vale, podemos quedarnos en casa y estudiar.	**Hoy me apetece ir al cine. ¿Quieres ir conmigo?** - Sí, me apetece. ¡Qué guay! ¿A qué hora quedamos? **Vamos a quedar enfrente del cine a las cinco y cuarto.** - ¡Fantástico! Hasta luego.	**¿Te gustaría hacer las tareas domésticas?** - Bueno, me apetece, pero tengo que trabajar. **Está bien. ¿Te gustaría trabajar juntos?** - Vale. ¿Dónde quedamos? **Quedamos enfrente del centro comercial.**

7	8	9
¿Quieres ir de tiendas conmigo? - Sí, me apetece. ¡Genial! ¿A qué hora quedamos? **Vamos a quedar enfrente del centro comercial a las siete menos diez.** - Está bien. Nos vemos luego.	**¿Te gustaría ir a casa de mis abuelos conmigo?** - Bueno, me apetece, pero no puedo. **¿Por qué no?** - Tengo que ayudar a mi padre y estudiar. **Vale. Está bien.**	**¿Qué te gustaría hacer mañana?** - Mañana tengo que ir a casa de Pablo. **¿Te gustaría dar una vuelta en el centro juntos?** - Sí, me gustaría. **Vale, nos vemos mañana.**

UNIT 12 – SURVEY

	¿Cómo te llamas? *What is your name?*	¿Qué quieres hacer este fin de semana? *What do you want to do this weekend?*	¿Qué quieres hacer mañana? *What do you want to do tomorrow?*	¿Te gustaría ir al parque conmigo? *Would you like to go to the park with me?*	¿Qué te gustaría hacer hoy? *What would you like to do today?*
e.g.	Me llamo Ben.	Me gustaría ir de tiendas.	Mañana quiero jugar al baloncesto.	Sí, me apetece, pero no puedo.	Hoy me gustaría estudiar.
1.					
2.					
3.					
4.					
5.					
6.					
7.					

UNIT 12 – ANSWERS

FIND SOMEONE WHO

	Find someone who...	Name(s)
1.	...wants to play basketball today.	Pablo/José
2.	...would like to go to the stadium today.	Miguel
3.	...has to go to Pablo's house this afternoon.	Paloma
4.	...fancies going to the park today.	Sergio/Julia
5.	...wants to go to their grandparents' house.	Victoria
6.	...wants to go for a walk in the city centre.	Harriet
7.	...wants to go to the cinema today.	Diego
8.	...has to work this afternoon.	Felipe
9.	...has to do household chores today.	Carlos
10.	...fancies going shopping this morning.	Gabriela
11.	...would like to play on the games console this afternoon.	Aurora
12.	...wants to help their mum today.	Amparo/Catalina
13.	...is a red herring! 🐟 (No match)	Julián

STAIRCASE TRANSLATION

¿Qué quieres hacer hoy? Hoy me gustaría ir de tiendas. ¿Te gustaría ir al parque conmigo? Bueno, me apetece, pero tengo que ayudar a mi madre. Está bien, podemos quedarnos en casa. ¿Dónde quedamos? Quedamos enfrente del cine a las seis y media.

FASTER!

REFEREE SOLUTION:

1. Hoy quiero jugar al baloncesto.   2. Lo siento, no me apetece.   3. Está bien, podemos jugar a la Play.
4. Bueno, me gustaría, pero tengo que trabajar.   5. ¡Genial! ¿Dónde quedamos?
6. ¿Qué quieres hacer esta tarde?   7. ¿Te gustaría ir a casa de Pablo conmigo?
8. Hoy me gustaría dar una vuelta en bici.   9. Vamos a quedar enfrente del cine a las cinco y media.
10. Bueno, me apetece, pero tengo que hacer las tareas domésticas.

FAST & FURIOUS

1. Hoy **me apetece** dar una vuelta en bici.   2. **Me gustaría** ir a casa de mis abuelos.
3. Hoy **quiero** ir al parque, pero tengo que estudiar.   4. Hoy quiero **jugar** a la Play.
5. Está bien, podemos **ir** al estadio.   6. Bueno, me apetece, pero tengo que **ayudar** a mi padre.
7. Vamos a **quedar** enfrente del cine.   8. ¿Qué quieres **hacer** esta tarde?   9. Lo siento, no **puedo**.
10. ¡Fantástico! ¿A qué hora **quedamos**?

Unit 13. (OPTIONAL) A future trip to Cádiz

¿Adónde vas a ir este verano?			*Where are you going to go this summer?*	
¿Cómo vas a viajar?			*How are you going to travel?*	
¿Dónde vas a quedarte?			*Where are you going to stay?*	
¿Qué vas a hacer?			*What are you going to do?*	
¿Qué lugares vas a ver/visitar?			*What places are you going to see/visit?*	

INSTRUCTIONS FOR ALL GAMES ARE ON PAGES 1-2

Este verano *This summer*	voy a ir *I'm going to go*	a Cádiz *to Cadiz*	Voy a viajar *I am going to travel* Vamos a viajar *We are going to travel*	en avión *by plane* en coche *by car*

El viaje *The trip*	El vuelo *The flight*	a España *to Spain*	dura X horas *takes X hours*

(No) Me gusta *I (don't) like*	viajar *to travel*	en avión *by plane* en barco *by boat* en coche *by car* en tren *by train*	porque es *because it is*	apasionante *exciting* cómodo *comfortable* divertido *fun* incómodo *uncomfortable* lento *slow* rápido *fast*

En Cádiz *In Cádiz*	voy a alojarme *I am going to stay* vamos a alojarnos *we are going to stay*	en *in*	un albergue *a hostel* un hotel *a hotel*	barato *cheap* básico *basic* caro *expensive* de lujo *luxury*

El hotel *The hotel*	está *is*	cerca *near* lejos *far*	del casco antiguo *from the old town* del centro *from the town centre* *del Puerto de Santa María *from the Port of Santa María* de la catedral *from the cathedral* de la playa de la Caleta *from the Caleta beach*

Durante el viaje	*During the trip*

me gustaría *I would like* voy a *I'm going* vamos a *we are going*	comer *to eat* probar *to try*	marisco *seafood* platos típicos *typical dishes* tapas *tapas*
	dar un paseo por *to go for a walk around* ver *to see* visitar *to visit*	el barrio de la Viña *the Viña neighbourhood* el casco antiguo *the old town* el Parque Genovés *the Genovés Park* el jardín botánico *the botanical gardens* la Plaza de las Flores *the flower market*

El primer día *On the first day* El segundo día *On the second day* Por la mañana *In the morning* Por la tarde *In the afternoon*	voy a ir *I am going to go* vamos a ir *we are going to go*	al museo *the museum* al parque *the park* a la playa *to the beach* a un espectáculo *to a show*

Finalmente *Finally*	voy a vamos a	volver a casa *go back home*	en autocar *by coach* en avión *by plane*	en coche *by car* en tren *by train*

Creo que el viaje a Cádiz será *I believe the trip to Cádiz will be*	genial *great* inolvidable *unforgettable*		la leche *awesome*

El viaje me hace mucha ilusión	*I'm really looking forward to the trip*

*Author's note: *El Puerto de Santa María* is a small town located on the bay of Cádiz, about 10km north east of Cádiz city, the region's capital. It is famous for its sherry, seafood and stunning beaches.

 THE LANGUAGE GYM

UNIT 13 – FIND SOMEONE WHO – Student Cards

Me gusta viajar en barco porque es divertido. **IÑAKI**	Creo que el viaje a Cádiz será la leche. **PEDRO**	En Cádiz, voy a alojarme en un hotel barato. **DIANA**	Me gustaría probar muchos platos típicos. **KARINA**
Durante el viaje voy a dar un paseo por el casco antiguo. **VICENTE**	El primer día voy a ir al parque. **CARMEN**	En Cádiz, voy a alojarme en un albergue básico. **LUISA**	Por la tarde voy a ir a la playa. **HECTOR**
Durante el viaje me gustaría comer marisco. **LUCÍA**	Me gustaría probar platos típicos. **ABEL**	Me gusta viajar en avión porque es muy cómodo. **SARA**	Me gusta viajar en tren porque es rápido. **ELLIE**
Me gusta viajar en avión porque es muy rápido. **MATT**	En Cádiz, voy a alojarme en un hotel de lujo con mi familia. **ANTONIO**	El segundo día vamos a ir al parque. **DARIO**	Me gusta viajar en tren, aunque a veces es incómodo. **FÁTIMA**

UNIT 13 – FIND SOMEONE WHO – Student Grid

¿Cómo vas a viajar? *How are you going to travel?* ¿Dónde vas a quedarte? *Where are you going to stay?*	
Find someone who...	**Name(s)**
1.	...likes to travel by plane.	
2.	...likes to travel by boat.	
3.	...likes to travel by train.	
4.	...is going to stay in a cheap hotel.	
5.	...is going to stay in a basic hostel.	
6.	...is going to stay in a luxury hotel with his family.	
7.	...would like to try typical dishes.	
8.	...would like to eat seafood.	
9.	...is going to go for a walk around the old town.	
10.	...is going to go to the beach in the afternoon.	
11.	...is going to go to the park on the second day.	
12.	...thinks the trip will be awesome.	
13.	...is a red herring! (No match)	

THE LANGUAGE GYM

UNIT 13 – ORAL PING-PONG – Person A

ENGLISH	SPANISH	ENGLISH	SPANISH
During the trip, I'm going to visit the Viña neighbourhood.	Durante el viaje voy a visitar el barrio de la Viña.	**I'm going to travel by boat.**	Voy a viajar en barco.
Where are you going to go this summer?		**The hotel is far from the centre.**	
During the trip, I would like to try seafood.	Durante el viaje me gustaría probar marisco.	**How are you going to travel?**	¿Cómo vas a viajar?
I like to travel by car because it is comfortable.		**I'm going to travel by plane.**	
During the trip, I'm going to try tapas.	Durante el viaje voy a probar tapas.	**In Cádiz, I'm going to stay in a basic hostel.**	En Cádiz voy a alojarme en un albergue básico.
In the morning, we are going to go to the park.		**Finally, we are going to go back home by train.**	
In Cádiz, I'm going to stay in a luxury hotel.	En Cádiz voy a alojarme en un hotel de lujo.	**During the trip, I'm going to try seafood.**	Durante el viaje voy a probar marisco.
What places are you going to visit?		**The hotel is far from the old town.**	
The hotel is near the Caleta beach.	El hotel está cerca de la playa de la Caleta.	**During the trip, I would like to see the botanical gardens.**	Durante el viaje me gustaría ver el jardín botánico.
What are you going to do?		**Finally, we are going to go back home by car.**	

UNIT 13 – ORAL PING-PONG – Person B

ENGLISH	SPANISH	ENGLISH	SPANISH
During the trip, I'm going to visit the Viña neighbourhood.		I'm going to travel by boat.	.
Where are you going to go this summer?	¿Adónde vas a ir este verano?	The hotel is far from the centre.	El hotel está lejos del centro.
During the trip, I would like to try seafood.		How are you going to travel?	
I like to travel by car because it is comfortable.	Me gusta viajar en coche porque es cómodo.	I'm going to travel by plane.	Voy a viajar en avión.
During the trip, I'm going to try tapas.		In Cádiz, I'm going to stay in a basic hostel.	
In the morning, we are going to go to the park.	Por la mañana, vamos a ir al parque.	Finally, we are going to go back home by train.	Finalmente, vamos a volver a casa en tren.
In Cádiz, I'm going to stay in a luxury hotel.		During the trip, I'm going to try seafood.	
What places are you going to visit?	¿Qué lugares vas a visitar?	The hotel is far from the old town.	El hotel está lejos del casco antiguo.
The hotel is near the Caleta beach.		During the trip, I would like to see the botanical gardens.	
What are you going to do?	¿Qué vas a hacer?	Finally, we are going to go back home by car.	Finalmente, vamos a volver a casa en coche.

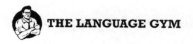

No Snakes No Ladders

7 I am going to travel by plane.	**6** In the afternoon, I'm going to go to a show.	**5** During the trip, I would like to see the botanical garden.	**4** During the trip, I'm going to try tapas.	**3** Where are you going to stay?	**2** During the trip, I'm going to try seafood.	**1** What places are you going to visit?
8 In Cádiz, I'm going to stay in a basic hostel.	**9** Finally, we are going to go back home by train.	**10** I am going to travel by car.	**11** The hotel is far from the old town.	**12** During the trip, I would like to visit the park.	**13** Finally, we are going to go back home by car.	**14** During the trip, I'm going to eat typical dishes.
23 The hotel is near the Caleta beach.	**22** What are you going to do?	**21** We are not going to stay in an expensive hotel.	**20** Where are you going this summer?	**19** During the trip, I would like to try seafood.	**18** The hotel is far from the centre.	**17** During the trip, I would like to go for a walk around the old town.
24 I am not going to stay in a basic hotel.	**25** On the second day, I am going to go to the museum with my dad.	**26** The hotel is far from the cathedral.	**27** How are you going to travel?	**28** I like to travel by train because it's fast.	**29** I like to travel by plane because it's comfortable.	**30** On the second day, we are going to go to the beach.

START

15 The hotel is near the town centre.

16 I don't like to travel by boat because it's slow and expensive.

FINISH

THE LANGUAGE GYM

No Snakes No Ladders

 SALIDA	2 Durante el viaje voy a probar marisco.	3 ¿Dónde vas a quedarte?	4 Durante el viaje voy a probar tapas.	5 Durante el viaje me gustaría ver el jardín botánico.	6 Por la tarde voy a ir a un espectáculo.	7 Voy a viajar en avión.
1 ¿Qué lugares vas a visitar?	13 Finalmente, vamos a volver a casa en coche.	12 Durante el viaje me gustaría visitar el parque.	11 El hotel está lejos del casco antiguo.	10 Voy a viajar en coche.	9 Finalmente, vamos a volver a casa en tren.	8 En Cádiz voy a alojarme en un albergue básico.
14 Durante el viaje voy a comer platos típicos.	13	18 El hotel está lejos del centro.	19 Durante el viaje me gustaría probar marisco.	21 No vamos a alojarnos en un hotel caro.	22 ¿Qué vas a hacer?	23 El hotel está cerca de la playa de la Caleta.
15 El hotel está cerca del centro.		17 Durante el viaje me gustaría dar un paseo por el casco antiguo.	20 ¿Adónde vas a ir este verano?			24 No voy a alojarme en un hotel básico.
16 No me gusta viajar en barco porque es lento y caro.	29 Me gusta viajar en avión porque es cómodo.	28 Me gusta viajar en tren porque es rápido.	27 ¿Cómo vas a viajar?	26 El hotel está lejos de la catedral.	25 El segundo día voy a ir al museo con mi padre.	
30 El segundo día vamos a ir a la playa.						LLEGADA

UNIT 13 – STAIRCASE TRANSLATION

This summer, I'm going to go to Cádiz. We're going to travel by plane.

This summer, I'm going to go to Cádiz. We're going to travel by plane because it is comfortable. The flight to Spain takes three hours.

This summer, I'm going to go to Cádiz. We're going to travel by plane because it is comfortable. The flight to Spain takes three hours. In Cádiz I'm going to stay in an expensive hotel.

This summer, I'm going to go to Cádiz. We're going to travel by plane because it is comfortable. The flight to Spain takes three hours. In Cádiz, I'm going to stay in an expensive hotel. The hotel is near to the old town.

This summer, I'm going to go to Cádiz. We're going to travel by plane because it is comfortable. The flight to Spain takes three hours. In Cádiz, I'm going to stay in an expensive hotel. The hotel is near to the old town. During the trip, I would like to try tapas.

This summer, I'm going to go to Cádiz. We're going to travel by plane because it is comfortable. The flight to Spain takes three hours. In Cádiz, I'm going to stay in an expensive hotel. The hotel is near to the old town. During the trip, I would like to try tapas. I think the trip to Cádiz will be unforgettable.

Translate the last step here:

THE LANGUAGE GYM

⏱️ UNIT 13 – FASTER! 🐦

Say:

1. This summer, I'm going to go to Cádiz.

2. I am going to travel by car.

3. I like to travel by boat because it is fun.

4. We are going to stay in a cheap hostel.

5. The hostel is near the Port of Santa María.

6. During the trip, I would like to eat seafood.

7. I'm going to go for a walk around the botanical gardens.

8. On the first day, I'm going to go to the beach.

9. Finally, we are going to go back home by coach.

10. I'm really looking forward to the trip.

	Time	Mistakes	Referee's name
1			
2			
3			
4			

UNIT 13 – THINGS IN COMMON

¿Qué prefieres?	1	2	3	4	5
¿Viajar en coche o avión?					
¿Ir de vacaciones a España o Francia?					
¿Quedarte en un hotel o un albergue?					
¿Comer marisco o tapas?					
¿Visitar el casco antiguo o el jardín botánico?					
¿Ir a la playa o al parque?					
¿Ir a una catedral o a un espectáculo?					

UNIT 13 – COMMUNICATIVE DRILLS

1	2	3
Where are you going this summer? - This summer, I'm going to go to France. **How are you going to travel?** - I like to travel by plane because it's fast and comfortable. However, we're going to travel by train.	**Where are you going to go this summer?** - This summer, I'm going to go to Spain with my family. **Great! Where are you going to stay?** - We're going to stay in a luxury hotel. It's close to the beach.	**What places are you going to visit?** - I'm going to visit the old town and the Viña neighbourhood. **Are you going to go for a walk around the old town?** - Yes, I would like to. It will be unforgettable.

4	5	6
What do you want to do in Spain? - I'm going to go to a show in the town centre. **Where are you going to stay?** - I'm going to stay in a hotel near the town square. **Great! It will be awesome.**	**This summer, I'm going to Portugal with my friends. And you?** - I'm going to Portugal, too. I'm going to try typical dishes. On the first day, I'm going to go to the beach. On the second day, I'm going to visit the cathedral.	**How are you going to travel to Spain?** - We're going to travel by boat. The trip to Spain takes twelve hours. It's slow! **What are you going to do on your trip?** - On the first day, we're going to the town centre. On the second day, we're going to visit the botanical gardens.

7	8	9
What are you going to do in Cádiz? - On the first day, in the morning, I'm going to go the park. In the afternoon, we're going to go the museum. Finally, we're going to go back home by coach. **I think the trip will be unforgettable.**	**What places are you going to visit?** - I'm going to go to the old town and the port. **What are you going to do?** - I'm going to eat seafood and try typical dishes. I'd like to try tapas.	**I'm going to take a walk around the old town and see the botanical gardens. And you?** - We're going to stay in an expensive hotel near the centre. I'd like to visit the museum.

UNIT 13 – COMMUNICATIVE DRILLS
REFEREE CARD

1	2	3
¿Adónde vas a ir este verano? - Este verano voy a ir a Francia. **¿Cómo vas a viajar?** - Me gusta viajar en avión porque es rápido y cómodo. Sin embargo, vamos a viajar en tren.	**¿Adónde vas a ir este verano?** - Este verano voy a ir a España con mi familia. **¡Genial! ¿Dónde vas a quedarte?** - Vamos a alojarnos en un hotel de lujo. Está cerca a la playa.	**¿Qué lugares vas a visitar?** - Voy a visitar el casco antiguo y el barrio de la Viña. **¿Vas a dar un paseo por el casco antiguo?** - Sí, me gustaría. Será inolvidable.

4	5	6
¿Qué quieres hacer en España? - Voy a ir a un espectáculo en el centro. **¿Dónde vas a quedarte?** - Voy a alojarme en un hotel cerca de la plaza mayor. **¡Genial! Será la leche.**	**Este verano voy a ir a Portugal con mis amigos. ¿Y tú?** - Voy a ir a Portugal también. Voy a probar platos típicos. El primer día voy a ir a la playa. El segundo día voy a visitar la catedral.	**¿Cómo vas a viajar a España?** - Vamos a viajar en barco. El viaje a España dura doce horas. ¡Es lento! **¿Qué vas a hacer en tu viaje?** - El primer día vamos a ir al centro. El segundo día vamos a visitar el jardín botánico.

7	8	9
¿Qué vas a hacer en Cádiz? - El primer día por la mañana voy a ir al parque. Por la tarde vamos a ir al museo. Finalmente, vamos a volver en autocar. **Creo que el viaje será inolvidable.**	**¿Qué lugares vas a visitar?** - Voy a ir al casco antiguo y al puerto. **¿Qué vas a hacer?** - Voy a comer marisco y probar los platos típicos. Me gustaría probar tapas.	**Voy a dar un paseo por el casco antiguo y ver al jardín botánico. ¿Y tú?** - Vamos a alojarnos en un hotel caro cerca del centro. Me gustaría visitar el museo.

UNIT 13 – SURVEY

	¿Cómo te llamas? *What is your name?*	¿Adónde vas a ir este verano? *Where are you going to go this summer?*	¿Cómo vas a viajar? *How are you going to travel?*	¿Dónde vas a quedarte? *Where are you going to stay?*	¿Qué vas a hacer? *What are you going to do?*	¿Qué lugares vas a visitar? *What places are you going to visit?*
e.g.	*Me llamo Miguel.*	*Este verano voy a ir a España.*	*Voy a viajar en coche.*	*Voy a alojarme en un hotel de lujo.*	*El primer día voy a ir a la playa.*	*Voy a visitar el casco antiguo.*
1.						
2.						
3.						
4.						
5.						
6.						
7.						

UNIT 13 – ANSWERS

FIND SOMEONE WHO

Find someone who...		Name(s)
1.	...likes to travel by plane.	**Sara/Matt**
2.	...likes to travel by boat.	**Iñaki**
3.	...likes to travel by train.	**Ellie/Fátima**
4.	...is going to stay in a cheap hotel.	**Diana**
5.	...is going to stay in a basic hostel.	**Luisa**
6.	...is going to stay in a luxury hotel with his family.	**Antonio**
7.	...would like to try typical dishes.	**Karina/Abel**
8.	...would like to eat seafood.	**Lucía**
9.	...is going to go for a walk around the old town.	**Vicente**
10.	...is going to go to the beach in the afternoon.	**Hector**
11.	...is going to go to the park on the second day.	**Dario**
12.	...thinks the trip will be awesome.	**Pedro**
13.	...is a red herring! 🐟 (No match)	**Carmen**

STAIRCASE TRANSLATION

Este verano voy a ir a Cádiz. Vamos a viajar en avión porque es cómodo. El vuelo a España dura tres horas. En Cádiz voy a alojarme en un hotel caro. El hotel está cerca del casco antiguo. Durante el viaje me gustaría probar tapas. Creo que el viaje a Cádiz será inolvidable.

FASTER!

REFEREE SOLUTION:

1. Este verano voy a ir a Cádiz.   2. Voy a viajar en coche.   3. Me gusta viajar en barco porque es divertido.
4. Vamos a alojarnos en un albergue barato.   5. El albergue está cerca del Puerto de Santa María.
6. Durante el viaje me gustaría comer marisco.   7. Voy a dar un paseo por el jardín botánico.
8. El primer día voy a ir a la playa.   9. Finalmente, vamos a volver a casa en autocar.
10. El viaje me hace mucha ilusión.

THINGS IN COMMON

Students give their own answers to the questions and make a note of which students they have things in common with.

Printed in Great Britain
by Amazon

42105152R00093